Mark Stewart-Jones is the author of five novels and two non-fiction titles. He has also co-written two graphic novels and edited two books of ghost stories for the Ghost Club, in addition to writing for *The Independent* amongst others. At times, he has also been a musician, a draughtsman and a rare-book dealer. For many years, Mark was the main carer for his daughter, Sophie. He currently divides his time between Canterbury, New Orleans and Paris. (Although he's intending to move to Charleville in the very near future!)

REAL LIFE IS ELSEWHERE

MARK STEWART-JONES

Matador
Unit E2 Airfield Business Park,
Harrison Road, Market Harborough,
Leicestershire. LE16 7UL
Tel: 0116 2792299
Email: books@troubador.co.uk
Web: www.troubador.co.uk/matador
Twitter: @matadorbooks

ISBN 978 1805141 938

British Library Cataloguing in Publication Data.
A catalogue record for this book is available from the British Library.

Printed and bound in Great Britain by 4edge Limited
Typeset in 11pt Minion Pro by Troubador Publishing Ltd, Leicester, UK

Matador is an imprint of Troubador Publishing Ltd

P.L.P.

1. Absence

Frivolity is another largely unanticipated casualty of middle age and I confess I miss it sometimes – in much the same way as I silently mourn the passing of any vaguely convincing enthusiasm for anything. Whereas both these qualities might once have seemed natural and spontaneous, there's an element of will power and subtle mental coercion involved nowadays. Whilst I suppose these are not significant markers of deterioration in themselves, there does seem to be the slight implication that the time has come to cast aside such blatantly immature diversions.

I don't know whether there is a gradual reduction in the capacity to act or respond frivolously or if you simply realise one morning that it has cruelly and permanently abandoned you. Gone. Boom! Just like that. So I apologise if this sounds a little forced – whilst the desire is still strong, the mechanism is sadly failing me today.

However, arriving on the first direct TGV from Gare de l'Est about half an hour ago, virtually the first thing I encounter (or rather do not encounter) disturbs me greatly, and once again, I repeat the five words to myself with my best attempt at mocking incredulity.

They have moved the duke!

And one more time.

They. Have. Moved. The. Duke.

It's true. He's no longer there, and there's simply no alternative reading. They've moved him, together with his plinth and his fountain, and replaced the whole edifice with a smaller, less flamboyant and altogether more anonymous water feature. All of which seems to suggest that the wise and fair-minded councillors have a far greater attachment to fountains in public spaces than they do to the aristocracy. Despite the fact that, from a historical perspective, such revolutionary ideas cannot be absolutely ruled out, I do fear that the actual reasoning in this particular case would be infinitely more mundane.

Admittedly, it's been twenty years since the last time I was here, but in a small, conservative town like Charleville, which exudes from every door, window, brick and paving slab a sense of sleepy permanence, you imagine things to be, well, yes, permanent. The duke was there, *right there*; a natural focal point, and now he's gone!

Thanks, Charleville.

Look it up if you don't believe me. The town was founded in 1606 by Charles Gonzaga, the eighth duke of Mantua, and La Place Ducale – the central square of the town – was named in his honour. In 1899, a statue of the man was erected at its centre. But now, the unthinkable has occurred – they have moved the duke. This is not good, I tell myself, this could be a very bad omen.

The lovely old chap has now vacated his spot in his eponymous place and has been relocated 100 metres or so up the road to reside next to Le Credit Lyonnaise. He has his back to Rimbaud's birthplace – perhaps intentionally, perhaps not – and he stares impassively down Avenue Jean Jaures towards the Place de la Gare (where still stands the bandstand immortalised

2

in one of Rimbaud's earlier poems 'À la Musique') and the symbol of all nineteenth-century advancement, industry and exploration: the grand old railway station.

That he looks pompous and ridiculous hardly warrants comment, as few people manage to achieve a look of modesty and self-effacement when cast in bronze.

For want of something to do, I wander over to the new, disappointingly impersonal fountain and dip my hand cautiously in the water. I'm more annoyed by this relocation than I should be. This being Charleville, of course, even the duke's absence resonates. It reminds me instantly of the story of Mérat refusing to be depicted alongside Rimbaud in Fantin-Latour's group portrait *Un Coin de Table*. He was subsequently painted out, and in his place, in order to maintain the overall composition of the canvas, Monsieur Fantin-Latour was forced to substitute a vase of flowers.

Absence.

We read absence in the life of Rimbaud; it is everywhere – the eternal subtext. The absent father; the lack of normal maternal affection. His long absences from the country of his birth. Even his own absence from literature or, rather, a distinguished literary career. (Remember, Rimbaud's entire life as a working poet is equalled by the time it took James Joyce to write half of *Finnegan's Wake*.) We can inhabit these absences; we can live and flourish, theorise, build, elaborate, and claim these absences – own these absences – because nothing remains to deny or to contradict. It all becomes worryingly subjective: behind this veil, he becomes *my* Rimbaud – my version, my vision.

The need to *explain* Rimbaud is often merely a device to mask the desire for sole ownership. It is the formula that renders him human and explicable – one that above all personalises him. The fact he is revealed to me brings about a tangible bond between us.

3

Now we both share the secrets for changing life.

Sadly, anyone who writes about Rimbaud inevitably writes about themself. So here I am in Charleville, writing notes for a book about Rimbaud and probably fooling no one.

Not least myself.

Just for the sake of disentangling myself briefly from my thoughts, I wander over to the ice-cream kiosk. I'm able to see the duke again now; there he is all the way down at the end of the road in his new location, silhouetted in the late-morning sun. Neglectful, absent father of this whole town! I turn away with as much adolescent disdain as I can muster and head down Rue du Moulin towards the old windmill.

As I walk, my thoughts once again return to that shortish introduction I was thinking about on the train. Just a couple of pages, I thought, outlining the basic biographical details of Rimbaud's life. Nothing emotive, no critical hyperbole – just cold dates and facts.

But how do I avoid sounding like Samantha?

That's the thing, isn't it?

Back in the late-eighties, I used to know a girl called Samantha. She was a pretty, freckly new-age-hippy type and as mad as makes no odds. We had a strange, undefined, impossible relationship, which just imploded one day under the weight of its own improbability. Samantha was given to periodic epiphanies, usually of a psychic or spiritual nature. Often, these were great insights into her life or grandiose predictions about her future. All coincidences in her life were given great magnitude or significance, and frequently over the most trivial of things.

Then, one day, she called on me to inform me that our 'off/on/mainly off' physical relationship would henceforth be terminated in favour of an entirely spiritual one, on account of her discovering something she attributed to the existence of God.

It was an afternoon I have never forgotten.

4

She explained her conversion with all necessary candour and conviction. 'Me and God,' she said by way of conclusion, 'have a great relationship.'

This line has lived with me for over thirty years. Not because I felt alarmed by her new evangelical sincerity or by her descent into religious zealotism but more on account of the billing: '*Me and God*', as though his was an entirely supporting or secondary role.

Samantha was the name on the cover of the album; God just sneaked into the credits on the back.

Therefore, a foreword suggests that, in some way, my subject is more obscure than I am and I'm simply offering this brief summary as a respectful literary courtesy. It is simultaneously a grotesquely patronising and insanely self-inflating idea – like some unwitting tribute to Henry fucking Miller. Besides, I am still convinced that however much I strive to avoid it, this whole project will inevitably descend periodically into something like 'Me and Rimbaud', and every time it does, I will think of Samantha.

And probably Henry Miller.

It is a beautiful, warm June day, and the air feels fresh and clear after Paris. Furthermore, dukes notwithstanding, Charleville seems superficially to be little changed in twenty years. Although I have noticed a few recent installations and monuments, presumably erected to mark the 150th anniversary in 2004 of Rimbaud's birth. To be honest, his profile in his hometown, on first impression, now seems significantly higher than it was at the end of the 1990s.

Maybe they have finally discovered the commercial possibilities of 'Rimbaud tourism' – remarked the Rimbaud tourist...

I finish the last of my ice cream, thrust my hands deep into my pockets (*les deux poings dans les poches* – even this simple gesture feels like an awkward homage) and glance in shop windows. If they are not precisely the same shops as before, they are similar enough, the dress shop was definitely there and that small tabac. A couple of hairdressers, both of which awkwardly reference Rimbaud in their window displays, seem recent, and there is a tattoo place that, without making any direct reference, almost insists we recall that line in his only published book, *Une Saison en Enfer*: '*Je me tatouerai, me veux devenir hideux comme un Mongol.*'[1]

I pass a few premises selling the usual unremarkable souvenirs, and amongst the predictable assortment of tea towels, crockery and glassware featuring the Ardennais boar, I see his face again. It is never far away here. It is inevitably a reproduction or artistic reimagining of the Etienne Carjat photograph of December 1871: the now universally recognised Rimbaud brand.

From the perspective of a fairly impartial (and usually disinterested) observer, it seems that the manufacturers of souvenirs the world over conform habitually to some general unspoken protocol and are driven consistently by consumer forces at least half a century out of date. As a consequence, one is forever being confronted by ashtrays, pipe racks and the like, rather than, say, smartphone cases.

Thus, I am observing what appears to be a virtually identical array of goods to those I encountered twenty years ago. At that time, I remember vividly being amazed, delighted and vaguely disappointed. At this distance, I can't quite recall what I might have been expecting, a short-run facsimile of the first edition of *Une Saison en Enfer*, maybe? But categorically not the 'Voyelles' tea towel, which is somehow both absurd and, in its own way, absolutely perfect – and, I note, still on sale.

And there is that face again!

This, by now, almost over-familiar image of the poet was captured two months after his seventeenth birthday. It matters

---

1   I will tattoo myself, I want to become hideous like a Mongol.

little that contemporary accounts and close associates always maintained that Carjat's first portrait of the poet, taken two months prior to the first, was by far the greater likeness. This fact is relegated to a footnote of little consequence. Perhaps this later depiction simply conforms more to our idea of a Poet. It is unquestionably a powerful and arresting image; with his mouth teetering on the brink of a sneer, he understands us, he has mapped our every thought and deed, and he loathes us with every fibre of his being. Even via the medium of obscure tableware he manages to look cold and distant.

Absent.

It is a face I have been looking at for forty years. For this image of Rimbaud is the mirror in which I have watched myself growing old.

Of course, that is the curse of the revolutionary. History will always have the final word. All radical ideas are ultimately processed, left to wither, and then reanimated, recast and used by advertising people to sell you products you neither want nor need – and once you've staggered blindly through yet another cyclone of shit, it all goes quiet again.

Ah yes, but those long-dead old gods were never yours.

I reach the end of the road and the corner property that my memory insists was a bar twenty years ago. Now, it is just a shuttered building with little evidence it was ever a commercial premises. Ever since that first visit, shutters have always made me think of Charleville and vice versa. Actually, speaking as a non-resident, I've always been troubled by shutters. Curtains imply you are doing something private, whereas – to my way of thinking – shutters always suggest you are doing something unspeakable and ghastly. I mean, just how much darkness do you actually need? Why bother with windows at all? To this day, whenever I walk past a shuttered window, I want to bang on it loudly and shout, 'I know what you're doing in there. You're doing something dark and medieval, something bad and possibly religious. Cut it out right now! Get yourself some blinds like decent people, you fucking ancient deviants…'

But the voice was never mine, of course; it's always been the one belonging to the rebellious and brilliant schoolboy with the mop of unruly hair…

I reach the junction at the end of Rue du Moulin, and I look over at the old windmill – nowadays, the Musée Rimbaud. The brickwork glows in the morning sun as it always does, like antique bronze, but I'm not ready to visit it just yet.

I think it is widely agreed by readers and critics alike that, at any point in his life, Rimbaud would have hated the idea of a museum in his honour. Particularly here in his hometown of Charleville, which he loathed without mercy and from which he couldn't wait to escape. Or, in truth, just be absent from.

'*Ma ville natale est supérieurement idiote entre les petites villes de province.*'[2] I hear Rimbaud say with the conviction born out of repetition.

I should state that I do feel a degree of sympathy with him about this. Provincialism, with its attendant frustrations and impatience, can sour a person's outlook. But it's always been my understanding that you have to hate the town where you grew up, its small mindedness, its petty values, its sense of confinement and its own self-importance – such sentiments are virtually compulsory. Like being vaguely ashamed of your parents, it's an absolutely key aspect of human development.

I stop and look away, feeling that my recently rediscovered talent for frivolity has chosen this moment to abandon me once more.

At the time of my previous visit, both my parents were still alive, and I'm not sure I'm quite ready to reflect upon that fact at this precise moment.

---

2   My home town is the most supremely idiotic of all small provincial towns.

2. Monument

I have no way of knowing if the experience is unique, common or universal (we tend to be notoriously disingenuous on the subject), but I never *discovered* Rimbaud in any conventional sense of the word; I simply collided with him at one particular point in my life, and nothing was the same thereafter. Perhaps *conversion* would be an overstatement, but in its own small way, there was something profound about that moment back in 1978. This wasn't art, not like I understood it to be. This was far beyond that; this was something toxic, radioactive even, and its effects would be permanent, far-reaching and entirely unpredictable.

I just had to wait and see how it would change me.

Tina, my first proper girlfriend, had studied Rimbaud as part of her A level French syllabus and had told me about him. This is the story I usually tell, but the truth is that, like so many people my age, I first heard of Rimbaud through Patti Smith, who in her own not-insignificant way has played a major role in promoting Rimbaud's literary reputation these past forty years, as much as Enid Starkie did in the forty years preceding that.

Oh, and whilst we're on the subject…

Three things you have to love about Enid Starkie:

Well, there is the name, of course. It is one of the great names of all time. Usually, you need to be a long-dead, black jazz musician to have such a great name: Dexter Gordon, Coleman Hawkins, Tadd Dameron, Hampton Hawes, Wardell Gray – the list is extensive. But *Enid Starkie* is definitely up there.

She was in no small part responsible for introducing Rimbaud to the English-speaking world. We all owe her a massive debt. At Oxford, she was instrumental in getting his work onto the French syllabus, and she wrote the first major biography of the poet in English in 1947.

Her *Arthur Rimbaud* is justly celebrated, and it remains a high-water mark of literary biography. It is incisive and fascinating, and for a whole generation, it will remain our first introduction to the life of the poet. But there are moments when she loses her academic objectivity and sounds a bit like an overindulgent aunt. It is almost as though she is seeking atonement on her subject's behalf and seems keen to gloss over his rebellious leanings, regarding them as little more than normal, healthy adolescent transgression and disdain for convention. This is evident if you see the original 1960 UK Faber hardback of the second edition. This particular version has the black-and-white plates absent from the subsequent paperback reprints. The reproduction of the second Carjat photograph is captioned 'Rimbaud In His Mystical Period'. Thus we are reassured and need not concern ourselves any more as it's evidently just a phase he's going through.

Thanks, Auntie Enid…

But in all honesty, if it weren't for you and your ground-breaking work, I would probably be a very different person, and I very much doubt I would be standing here in the lobby of this particular hotel on a beautiful June day, waiting to get checked in.

The Hôtel Couleurs Sud, in which I have booked myself a single room for a couple of days, is located on the northern side of the Place de la Gare and is less than a minute's walk from the station. However, such convenience played no part whatsoever in my decision-making process. My choice was based entirely (and a little obviously) on the fact that this particular hotel is situated right next to the Bar de l'Univers, and Rimbaud was known to have frequented the bar (although it was the *Café* de l'Univers in his day). According to several sources, it was here that he would famously recite – in exchange for a drink or two – outrageous, graphically detailed and largely invented tales of his exploits. The building was modernised at some point and rendered fairly anonymous, so it lacks the sort of decaying bourgeois splendour that is so much in evidence around Charleville, but it still forms in my mind a vague yet satisfying sense of connection.

The lady behind the desk is still gazing at her monitor as she has been engaged these past few minutes in trying to find any evidence or record of my online booking. At least, I hope that is what she is doing, but I can't be sure. So I lean forwards and rest my elbows on the counter as casually as I can in the hope of reminding her of my existence. She narrows her eyes and glances once again at the name on my credit card; I'm struggling to recall the French word for 'hyphen'.

'*C'est Stewart, peut-être?*' I offer eventually.

'*Un moment, Monsieur,*' she replies brusquely, without looking at me.

'Ahhh…' she utters eventually, her expression being perfectly pitched at some previously unknown mid-point between delight and disgust.

There is now also the vaguest suggestion of a smile, and she begins to nod. All of which I take to be a positive sign. As a concluding gesture, she taps the monitor victoriously with her index finger, and it is then that I notice the collection of bracelets and wristbands on her arm for the first time. For a second, I think of Djibouti and the Abyssinian mistress…

'*Ah oui, Monsieur, vous êtes* ici. *Pas de problème.*'

'*Bon, merci,*' I reply with a genial, non-committal, international shrug.

She says something then that I don't quite grasp, although I recognise the word '*valise*' and I assume she is enquiring about luggage.

I indicate my rucksack (containing underwear, a washbag, one reasonably new tablet with charger and adaptor, four T-shirts, one recent biography, an old prose translation of the poetry and a highly regarded verse translation from 2002) on my shoulder.

'*C'est tout…*' I say with a smile.

'*…D'accord,*' she says, eying me with suspicion for a moment.

Then, with a flourish, she hands me the room key and the code for the Wi Fi and then points me in the direction of the lift.

Room 307 is at the front of the hotel and therefore looks out over the Place de la Gare. It is not a grand or particularly noteworthy room by any stretch of the imagination; it is fairly small, and if one wished to be cruel, one could say 'basic', but it's clean, smells fresh and caters to all my particular needs.

The room is in darkness when I enter, so I push aside the nets and the heavy drapes and open the window, allocating a bonus point to Hôtel Couleurs Sud in the process for not forcing me to endure the vileness of shutters for the duration of my stay.

I close my eyes and inhale the moment. When I open them again, I am looking out over the square. I find myself smiling.

Beyond the tiny, wrought-iron, ornamental balcony, across the street below and between the two great conifer trees, I can see him again. He stares directly at me, eyeball to eyeball, daring me, accusing me, mocking me and amusing himself at my expense. Am I surprised to see him? Who was I expecting to see? Why do you think they keep the curtains drawn?

I just forgot…

'*Merde!*'[3]

Ah yes, and there you are again!

The old, original bust of Rimbaud – which is in the square, opposite the station and just a short distance away from the bandstand – is a matter of fifty metres or so from my window. I think it's probably fair to say that the monument says more about Charleville than it does about Rimbaud. Reclaimed by the town of his birth and rendered in bronze, his infamy momentarily cast aside, he strikes an oddly formal figure, but at least he hasn't undergone the indignity of relocation. There is a certain stately nobility about this particular Rimbaud: strong and taciturn, a man of the highest moral character, and furthermore – lest we forget – a citizen of this fine town. Upstanding and dependable. Just like us. Actually, I've always thought he simply looks bored and maybe we should read something into that? Or perhaps he has just grown weary of his strange, side-parted 1940's haircut?

'*Les goûts frivoles m'ont quitté.*'[4]

Nah, I have never recognised this guy. He is just another version of another version, and he is not mine. Literally, the current bust dates from the 1950s and replaced one that was lost in the war, which in turn had replaced one erected in 1924 after the original 1901 sculpture was taken by Germans at the end of the First World War. This first bust had been unveiled to commemorate the tenth anniversary of his death, and although she was still living in Charleville at that time, Rimbaud's mother refused to attend the ceremony. Nor, it is said, did she ever visit the monument, even though she lived for a further six years in an apartment no more than a stone's throw away.

---

3   Shit!
4   Frivolous tastes have abandoned me.

'*Ah… La Bouche d'Ombre…*'[5]

Indeed. And even in the most cursory reading of Rimbaud's life, one inevitably stumbles upon the endless, impenetrable, widow-black shadow cast by his mother. It's an issue I'm planning to ignore for the time being. I don't want to think about his mother – or anyone's mother, for that matter. It would then be too easy for me to think of my own.

It has been five months now, and recently, Selfishness and Recrimination have reared their ugly heads: You failed me; you didn't do your job or keep your side of the bargain, did you? Look at me! I'm not a grown-up; I am nowhere near a grown-up! I have never been prepared for this adult life, and I am struggling. Where are my coping skills, Mother, or my well-tuned, mature objectivity in all this? Why did you never explain all this to me? Why don't I know how to deal with these things? Why did you leave me in this useless, infantile state? I'm just not ready, and no, you are not excused; your task was not completed! You gave up on me. OK, I'm not saying you were negligent, but why do I find that maturity, in my case, is solely a measure of time and not experience? Why don't I have all those necessary qualities? All the things I need to get through this. Why can't I cope with you not being here any more? Why do I need things to help me sleep? Did you feel like this when you lost *your* mother? I need to ask you… I need… you.

Now do you see my problem?

'*La Bouche…*'

Oh shut up!

I take my washbag into the bathroom and start putting its contents mechanically on shelves. I look at my reflection, but every thought that crosses my mind is the sort of terrible cinematic or literary cliché I would never wish to record. I run the tap and splash some water on my face before deciding that might be somewhat a cliché too.

---

5   Ah… The Mouth Of Shadows…

I kick off my shoes and stretch out on the bed.

So, from what dim, dark recess of the soul does this instinct emanate? This sudden, recent enthusiasm for didactic self-flagellation? This ongoing compulsion to revisit, re-examine and articulate my own pain. Is it some laughably optimistic theory that the repetition will somehow diminish the agony? Having failed to construct a credible excuse, I have been left pondering whether this is just something else to do with my age. So far, the only consolation of ageing I have discovered is the opportunity to relive all your previous catastrophes and failures from the deeply gratifying perspective of having already survived them.

That and sleep...

Therefore, I doze for twenty minutes and lose myself in a complicated dream, the narrative of which somehow features both The Stranglers and Boris Johnson. Although the possible Jungian subtext is deeply appealing, their appearance together was of less consequence to me upon awakening than the fact that the entire episode had taken place in the playground of my old school. Yet again. For nowadays, I dream all too frequently of my school and must therefore sadly conclude that it still lurks darkly in my subconscious. I hated that school, and I think I may actually hate it even more with hindsight. Looking back at my youth, I have never blamed my parents for my failures or my shortcomings or my lack of confidence or my poor choices in everything. Thus ignoring what might be considered the more traditional route, I have simply dedicated the considerable sum total of my inadequacies to my education generally and thereafter to my school specifically.

I am hence blameless and misunderstood.

God, how I wish I could tell you it was some great, venerable, old, red-bricked public school! But no, mine was just another unremarkable and unlovely comprehensive school in South Wales. One for which it's fair to say that, in the 1970s, 'it was going through an identity crisis', an affliction it passed on to a vast number of its pupils – me included. The year it actually made its transition from an old secondary modern school to a bold new comprehensive coincided unfortunately with my first year there.

The teaching staff were fairly evenly divided between the new influx of progressively minded, ambitious younger teachers who saw great potential in the school and the older, less academically orientated staff who had seen more than their fair share of difficult pupils and unruly classrooms. It amounted to nothing less than an academic turf war, and who could flourish in such an environment? Not me for one. For I was certainly no academically gifted student, like the young Rimbaud, but I maintained my interest in Art and English and I held down reasonable grades for most of my time there.

In the lower sixth, my Art class was set an essay about how the saleability of artists' work was in some way representative of their value. (I hated the word 'saleability'. It sounded like a truly comprehensive-school word and was therefore something to fear.) I wrote about 1,000 words before I eventually concluded that 'saleability' was entirely irrelevant, yet it might be a method by which an artist judges his own merits. My teacher singled out this phrase and gave me a big tick in the margin, but then asked me to back up my assertion with an example – which, of course, I couldn't.

However, I have been haunted by that essay for almost four decades. I have, on occasion, applied its underlying themes to Rimbaud, but more frequently, I confess, I apply them to myself. For my own purposes, I define myself as a writer inasmuch as I have self-published half a dozen novels over the years. I've had one or two good reviews in that time, plus a few nice comments on Amazon, but not enough sales – if I am honest – to justify the general mad conceit of it all. Saleability, you see, idiot sixteen-year-old version of me, is a major consideration after all! And again, speaking from experience, there is precious little comfort to be had in basking in any sense of personal integrity or in one's fondly imagined purity of vision.

But still, I consider myself a writer by virtue of the fact that I do not consider myself anything else.

So, I seem doomed to remain eternally at the same point Rimbaud was in the late 1880s, prior to his work being published in Paris by Verlaine for the first time; a few good notices and a self-published book, but other than that, rejection and obscurity.

Absence, in other words.

He was in his twenties at the time whilst I am now in my fifties – but, I keep telling myself, the same principle applies.

We are brothers…

I wander back towards the window and look out over the Place de la Gare once again. He is still there, sneering at me.

'*Merde!*'

I nod slowly in agreement.

3. Formula

One seldom-discussed aspect of Charleville, which should be more openly celebrated, is the fact that its general compact size and road layout make it the perfect town for any disgruntled, street-prowling, nocturnal teen. Speaking as one who, for many years, rejected more social pursuits in favour of solitary evening walks around his hometown, I can claim to have some experience in these matters. Charleville is perhaps the most perfect location I have ever visited for this purpose. Its narrow, largely deserted, dimly lit streets in a block system mean you have an infinite number of circuits available with very little traffic to muffle or drown out your thoughts and footsteps.

In search of lunch, I leave the Hôtel Couleurs Sud and walk away from the Place de la Gare. I then make a left turn into Rue de l'Arquebuse and head towards the centre of town. Rimbaud, from the age of ten, attended L'Institution Rossat at number 11 on this street, and I can so easily imagine that this was part of his regular route. I picture a scene at twilight: nothing more than a silhouette; a shuffling, determined gait; in ill-fitting boots and clothes he was rapidly growing out of; and with his mind ever occupied by planning his next escape or simply refining lines of verse.

'*J'égrenais dans ma course des rimes.*'[6]

In fact, it is certainly possible that his great poetic doctrine was honed whilst walking these very streets. At the age of sixteen, in May 1871, he set out these theories in two letters, one to each of Messieurs Izambard and Demeny; these are the legendary *Lettres du Voyant*, which remain among the most discussed and important documents in the history of French literature.

In these two remarkable letters, the second being a more expanded version of the first, Rimbaud puts forward his artistic creed and the system by which he will create anew the whole function and nature of poetry. They are, by any literary criteria, extraordinary, revolutionary texts.

One of the key aspects to the letters – which is central to Rimbaud's thinking – is his assertion that a true poet must transform himself into a seer or a visionary (*voyant*), and this is achieved, he stresses, by experiencing all manner of suffering, torture and madness; all kinds of love; and every type of poison. At which point, he arrives at the unknown (*l'inconnu*) – his ultimate goal and purpose. He summarises this quest, in one of his most notorious and endlessly quoted lines, as '*une long, immense etraisonné* dérèglement *de* tous les sens' (the emphases are in Rimbaud's original).

To some, this amounts to nothing less than the $E=mc^2$ of modernity.

However, it was the fourth and the fifth words of this famous line that troubled me when I was younger. In various anthologies or studies, I have read the words translated as the following:

Logical derangement

Rational disordering

Systematic disorganisation

---

6   I scattered my path with rhymes.

Reasoned disorientation

So it is, in essence, '*a long, intense, systematic derangement of all the senses*'. It took me a long time to understand this fully; for many years, I found it paradoxical and almost oxymoronic. 'Systemic derangement' seemed to me to be perilously close to 'organised disorder', and I consistently failed to appreciate fully the interpretations of critics and biographers. To be honest, I found this single detail silly and almost annoying, maybe even childish.

I reach number 11 and am disappointed to discover that I am gazing at a fairly anonymous, drab, modernish facade. It is so different to that sly implication of half-forgotten historic opulence so often witnessed in this town and even in the buildings on this same street. It is fairly unique in this respect and looks oddly out of place. Indeed, it jars, and I wonder if, at some point, the street numbers have been reassigned. Although I was not sure what I was expecting, I feel momentarily irritated by both the dull building and my keenness to locate it.

But there is absolutely nothing here for me – no trace and no vibrations.

Going back to the aforementioned quote, I eventually allowed myself to be convinced that Rimbaud's classic quote and the letter from which it came were less of a literary manifesto and more of a formula. Or an equation. For Rimbaud didn't simply want to be a poet (in his own mind, he was already a poet and had been for years), he wanted to entirely reinvent the very meaning of poetry.

And inventions require formulas.

In fact, so much of Rimbaud's life can be read as a quest for a formula of some sort: for poetry, for business and for life. In many of his poems, we find references to alchemy, and in some respects, this was maybe how the poet metaphorically viewed both himself and the career upon which he'd embarked.

So is this going to be the message? My final insight? My

epiphany? Is this the motif of the man's life finally made manifest to me? Is this now the purpose behind my visit? Impulse and intuition are for amateurs and hobbyists, you fool, whereas genius relies on pure method! It is a method that also dictates how and when something as worthless as instinct or as trivial as inspiration is processed.

I have always thought that, in Rimbaud's finest work, there is a brutal, mathematical precision and clarity that is simultaneously both beautiful and terrifying. Of course, it is also absolutely perfect in its own way, but this perfection is only a testimony to the strict method underlying it. His imagination was honed and trained in a manner even Nietzsche could barely have conceived.

By comparison, I wander around a little town in a foreign country, looking at old buildings and waiting to feel inspired. Then I look at them again, I gaze up at the sky a bit and I think I should get something to eat.

My perspective on Rimbaud is permanently shifting and has done for many, many years – and ironically, this is one of the few certainties in my life. Without lapsing into too much dreary self-analysis, I do fully understand that this is one of the main reasons why I am actually here in Charleville. This year of my mother's death has coincided with the continuing turmoil of Brexit and the unending catastrophe of Donald Trump. Therefore, writing about Rimbaud is not activity or creativity, it is simply a warm, safe place I know and where I want to be.

You see, Rimbaud is like this: Rimbaud is different from Joyce, Dickens, Wolfe, Hemingway and Kerouac even! They all have readers, scholars and enthusiasts, but not Rimbaud! Rimbaud has *fans*! And to his fans, he is the puzzle, the cipher, the permanent ongoing investigation.

Rimbaud is the JFK assassination of French Poetry.

Now I am perhaps gradually starting to understand this need for the formula – in life and in art. Maybe I'm just stumbling towards my own version of my own equation? More than I am perhaps prepared to admit, I need Rimbaud in my life at the moment. But in fairness, I also need the first Clash album, Robert Johnson, a stack of Blue Note stuff, The Ramones' *Leave Home* and *Charlie Parker on Dial*. All of which are currently on both my phone and my tablet.

I suppose traditionally *men of a certain age*, by which I mean men of my age, succumb to all manner of temptations and all kinds of stupidity. Mainly because, everywhere we turn, we see endings and conclusions when all we so desperately crave is that one great beginning.

Or just the very merest suggestion that it's not all behind us and there is still some great unchartered road for us to race down.

Barefoot.

I wander towards the main thoroughfare, wondering if Rimbaud would accuse me of failing to understand him or if I am attempting somehow to make a virtue out of embracing my own mediocrity. *Embrassant la médiocrité!* I smile awkwardly with little or no sense of amusement at this and walk a little quicker.

Following this vague train of thought, when I reach Rue de la République, I am thinking – possibly for the first time in thirty years – about Cardiff City Football Club. My parents moved to Cardiff when I was very young, and I grew up about three miles away from Ninian Park, which was then the home of Cardiff City (it has since been demolished and rebuilt nearby). I was so desperate to go to a match that I bothered my father constantly, but he refused to take me. Instead, my grandfather was eventually talked into dragging me along to a couple of games. It was an absolutely thrilling experience for me at the time.

However, the thing I remember most from those Saturday afternoons was the singing. It was just amazing. Joining in with the chanting of thousands of fellow fans was unlike anything I'd ever experienced, and I loved the feeling of being part of a loud mass of like-minded people for once. Obviously, I practised discretion during some of the more expletive-laden chants – I was with my grandfather after all. Many of these chants are common to all football grounds and to all teams, but nowhere other than Cardiff have I heard that fans actually chanted, as they did at Ninian Park, 'Ooooh, It's A Corner; Ooooh, It's A Corner!' Honestly, that's what we used to chant whenever we got a corner! Clearly, when Cardiff City was playing this was considered an achievement worthy of celebration.

'Ooooh, It's A Corner...'

And that's today's lesson and your essential life skill right there!

That's the dharma of Ninian Park!

The secret to divine fulfilment and to all human happiness is simply the capacity to delight in mundanity, pointlessness, and all that is existentially and uncontrovertibly self-evident. Fuck Rimbaud! Why quest after the unknown or after certainty when all attainment is illusory? Don't push your boundaries or launch yourself at the unobtainable, just find something thrilling and uplifting in your own ordinariness. Kick off your shoes and dance all night to the smooth relaxing sounds of your own worthlessness!

Altogether now...

'*Ooooh, it's a corner...*'

There is a seemingly infinite number of small cafés located in the colonnade that circles the perimeter of La Place Ducale, and I select one more or less at random. I buy a coffee and a sandwich from a smiling waitress and sit at an outside table. I idle away a few minutes by observing the fair people of Charleville as they make their way through the square. A good few, I notice, are walking at a faster pace with what I take to be a more determined sense of purpose, and I assume that these are returning to work after lunch. I do a quick, less than meticulous calculation in my head and conclude that I am possibly observing the great-great-great-great-grandchildren of the very townspeople that Rimbaud despised and was so vitriolic in condemning.

I take a thoughtful bite out of my sandwich and wonder how I would feel if I had to shoulder a legacy of that magnitude. Actually, they all seem like perfectly friendly, perfectly decent people to me, but being a Rimbaud *fan* means that I, like so many others, remain exclusively sympathetic to his point of view. Indeed, everything else is relegated in significance to mere context or background. We are very harsh and very selective in our judgements, and we identify ourselves solely with the object of our obsession.

As a good example of this, I could cite the events of 24th September 1871, a matter of four months after the *Lettres du Voyant*.

That day should have been a significant and noteworthy day in the history of French literature as it marked the first meeting of Rimbaud and Verlaine. Rimbaud had sent the older poet examples of his work and was, as a result, invited to come to Paris. But on the day of his arrival, Verlaine was drunk and in a state of panic. Uncertain of the station at which the train from Charleville was arriving, he had oscillated between Gare du Nord and Gare de l'Est, which are in fact only a little more than 200 metres apart. In doing so, he managed to miss Rimbaud's arrival, and so the great meeting was postponed until later in the day.

I know that we have all visualised this so many times!

There's Verlaine, weak-willed and befuddled in his drunken confusion. But then we see Rimbaud in the distance, striding off confidently in the direction of Verlaine's house on Rue Nicolet in Montmartre. Rimbaud is our feral peasant savage, a month shy of his seventeenth birthday and skinny but physically strong, with his wild, unkempt, long hair. He has no luggage, but in his pocket, he is carrying the manuscript of 'Le Bateau Ivre'

– arguably the most important of his early poems. We have all read the biographies, and we have lived this moment with him.

The following scene, which takes place on Rue Nicolet that afternoon, is one of our all-time favourites. One of the quintessential Rimbaud tableaux! Verlaine remains absent and otherwise occupied, and so Rimbaud is invited into the house by Mathilde – Verlaine's young wife, who was roughly Rimbaud's age (and who would subsequently come to loathe the ruffian from the provinces) – and Mathilde's mother. There follows a classic sequence where the ladies' polite conversational enquiries are met by Rimbaud's monosyllabic surliness. He smokes his pipe and can barely hide his disgust at the company and his surroundings.

It's a perfect moment for the committed Rimbaud fan. We naturally share his view; we see everything through his narrowed, pale-blue eyes; and we feel his rage, his loathing and his discomfort. When he directs his anger at the family pet and utters his only recorded quote of the afternoon – '*Les chiens, ce sont des libéraux*' – we obviously endorse his sentiments.

We sneer along with him at the ghastly bourgeois spectacle being played out in front of him. This vile middle-class drawing room with its ridiculous ornaments and its wretched fixtures and fittings. We can smell the wood polish, the misery and the sense of confinement. With no effort whatsoever, we can imagine the pictures on the wall. Personally, I can see a dark, unremarkable oil painting or two; perhaps a formless neo-classical landscape with what might be an obscure biblical theme. This might be hung alongside a portrait of some distant, esteemed relative – a stiff and serious worthy bureaucrat - long dead but regularly dusted. Then in the corner, just above the potted fern, there is that bucolic hunting scene rendered in the brownest and most dismal of palettes. God, if we think hard enough, we can even picture the terrible floral-print wallpaper – or was it a Regency stripe?

Whatever Rimbaud was expecting this was not it; in his mind, this was not the home of a poet, much less an environment for a seer or a *voyant*. This was actually little different to Charleville. The ladies make him tea and ask him polite questions about his family. But we hate them and their stupid values, don't we? We simply see the mumbling, slouched figure, the prototype of everyone who has ever mattered to us, the rebel…

OK, stop now, just drag yourself away for moment. I know we are all so familiar with the scene and have lived it so many times, but just for a second, look away from Rimbaud. Come on, I know you can do it – just give me a minute. He's fine, so leave him; just direct your attention towards the two ladies – can you do that for me? Please? I know, in your mind, they are probably both dressed in black and knitting or something, but just bear with me.

Now, not her, not the wife; forget about her. I want you to focus on the older lady. Yes, the one you've decided looks like *Whistler's Mother*; that's the one, yeah – her. Verlaine's mother-in-law, Madame Mauté…

No, just stop thinking about Rimbaud. I know what he thinks of her, but *please* just stay over here with me for a second.

Now, this lady right here – come on, just look at her. She is actually a very accomplished musician; you didn't know that, did you? No, of course you didn't. Do you want to know something else interesting about her? I thought not, but I'm going to tell you anyway. You see, before she was just a walk-on in our favourite Rimbaud vignette, she had been a pupil of Chopin. Not the slightest clue again, am I right? Yeah? Furthermore, at this particular point in her life – yes, at this very moment – she is also giving piano lessons to the young Claude Debussy, something for which he would remain grateful for the rest of his life. So, let's just freeze the image and keep her in shot for a second or two, OK? That's good. Stay with her and maybe bring the music up on the soundtrack a bit? Yeah, that works for me…

You see, Rimbaud fan, he was not the only person of artistic or cultural interest at 14 Rue Nicolet that afternoon, but you really have to hunt around for that information. (Besides, we don't want anyone casting any sort of shadow over our boy, now do we?) Starkie mentions Debussy, but not Chopin, and many ignore Madame Mauté's story altogether. In fact, the three most recent Rimbaud biographies of any consequence make no reference to this detail whatsoever, preferring instead to analyse and deconstruct Rimbaud's comment about dogs being liberals.

Pauvre Mme. M.

I guess she never really stood a chance.

A few minutes pass, and I vacate my table at the café and mingle with the great-great-great-great-grandchildren once more.

4. MODERN

In 'Adieu', the final section of *Une Saison en Enfer*, Rimbaud famously wrote '*Il faut être absolument modern.*'[7] It is another phrase that has long been associated with the poet and, again, one that suggests a sworn declaration of purpose – a simple but dynamic assurance that has chained itself to its creator in the minds of so many.

To us, it is a manifesto written in stone – not just figuratively or metaphorically but also, in this case, quite literally.

In actual fact, the precise quote is right here in front of me, inscribed into the base of the fairly recently erected statue of Rimbaud located about 100 metres or so up the road from the Musée Rimbaud. I have read about it and seen photographs online, but this is the first time I have actually encountered it in reality. This is not entirely a chance meeting, but after lunch, with no particular objective in mind, I had wandered down towards the river and then just ambled in its general direction.

The larger-than-life-size sculpture can be seen at the

---

7   One must be absolutely modern.

entrance to the Collège Arthur Rimbaud, a newly renamed public middle school, which caters for pupils as young as eleven. Consequently, I'm sure I share with most visitors a slight sense of discomfort when contemplating anything for any length of time (also known as 'hanging around') in such close proximity to a school gate.

But the statue is an impressive piece in many ways and a suitable enough counterpoint to the rather more formal representation at Le Place de la Gare. This newer Rimbaud is far nearer to our Fantasy Rimbaud – all the details are here! He rests his head on his hand and has the physical characteristics of a young boy.

'*Les poètes de sept ans?*'[8]

I suppose that's possible, although it seems a little obvious and overly literal. Beyond question is the fact he is growing out of his clothes, is also bare-chested and barefooted, and holds a pen in his left hand. Once again, for all time, with his wild unkempt hair, we are presented with the Chimera Rimbaud – the one that reflects, perhaps in mockery, all our silly ideas back to us.

Our wonderful vagabond, urchin poet in all his glory.

God bless him.

But for some reason, today, I actually find this representation a little irritating. Beyond any artistic misgivings, there now seems to be something almost medieval about this particular take on Rimbaud – repetition drifts into familiarity, which drifts into tradition, and this is the Rimbaud for the ages. The Timeless Rimbaud. The reimagined boy-ghost of François Villon. A shiver passes through me. Sorry, but I admit I am, yeah, you know, well, more than a little familiar with this Rimbaud...

'*Merde!*'

Yeah, I know...!

---

8   The seven-year-old poets.

He stares down at me, daring me to question if this image could truly qualify as anyone's concept of 'absolutely modern'. I shake my head. This is not artistically all that distant from the silly old duke atop his fountain! With no effort whatsoever, I think, this Rimbaud could take his place alongside the cavorting peasants in a Breughel painting.

'*J'aimais les peintures idiotes...*'[9]

Don't change the subject.

Suddenly, I feel uneasy, unnerved, fleetingly confused, annoyed or depressed; I don't quite know what it is or why it might actually matter. But the truth is that this touches on something that has troubled me periodically for a long time. It is generally accepted, not just amongst his loyal fans, that Rimbaud is one of the great precursors of modernism. (It is an accolade he shares with, amongst others, Van Gogh, whose lifespan – allowing for a one-year shift forwards – perfectly mirrors Rimbaud's own.) So whilst we insist on viewing Rimbaud in this bizarrely antiquarian manner, are we (am I?) subconsciously attempting to magnify this achievement? It does seem to reflect our perceptions and the overall narrative, I suppose; this is our marvellous Antediluvian Rimbaud – the ancient and eternal voice of all generations, the inventor, and the originator – and he cannot be contained by anything as bourgeois and restrictive as dates and times.

(I said we were *fans*, didn't I?)

Rimbaud was born in 1854. Oscar Wilde was actually born in the same week, but somehow, he seems to have been allowed to exist in his own time and take his place amongst those of his own generation.

OK, here's another one. The composer John Philip Sousa was born two weeks after Rimbaud, and he lived until 1932. Now imagine if Rimbaud had lived that long. Imagine him writing about Cubism and the Dadaists. Imagine a book review

---

9   I loved idiotic paintings...

for *Ulysses*, an essay on jazz or cinema, a photograph with Andre Breton or Modigliani, Rimbaud driving a car, Rimbaud on the phone...

These are not ideas that can be entertained easily when forced to confront something like this barefooted, raggedy character towering over me. I step away from its shadow and, over my shoulder, I sneer in little above a whisper, 'Your brother was a fucking bus driver, ducky; let's not forget that...'

'*Pitoyable frère!*'[10]

'Yeah, and you know what? I'm not convinced there's actually any hard evidence that you were left-handed either...'

I walk away as something cosmic or something sub-atomic shifts in space or time, and once again, I feel abandoned, orphaned, marooned and no longer connected to my own certainties.

My own *sense of things*.

This Rimbaud – this perpetual, infinite vagrant teenager – seems to have always existed for me (and for others too, evidently) on a timeline that seems vastly more emotional than actually chronological. The only other example of this I have encountered in practise (and of which I might also be judged guilty) would be in the enduring popular portrayal of the great Mississippi bluesman, Robert Johnson. Like Rimbaud, Johnson was another enormously significant artist and another radical innovator whose singular genius is almost obscured by the fanciful and durable myths that have gathered around him after his death. Both artists sought to articulate, or even celebrate, existential despair, often referencing biblical imagery, and both worked with themes that set them apart from their immediate peers. And like Rimbaud, Johnson's reputation rests upon a fairly small body of work that was executed over a relatively brief time period. He recorded only twenty-nine songs over a

---

10   Pitiful brother!

handful of sessions between 1936 and 1937, and the resulting seventy-eights generated only local interest in his lifetime. When he died in 1938 at the age of twenty-seven, his work was also comparatively obscure and known only to those with a specialist interest in the subject. Again, in the true spirit of Rimbaud, his reputation has been almost entirely posthumous. In 1961, an LP compilation of some his original recordings was issued, and this proved to be a massively significant event. This record remains a cornerstone of the music of the latter half of the twentieth century and a lasting influence on so many musicians.

Johnson, like Rimbaud, was rescued from relative oblivion and judged retrospectively to be one of the greatest creative forces of his generation. But again, equal to the art, it is so often the obscurity that appeals to us. We are drawn into the huge, yawning plot holes in the story. Why did Rimbaud *really* stop writing? How did Robert Johnson learn to play the guitar like that? If *Une Saison en Enfer* is truly the work of a self-defining atheist or a pagan, why use such a Christian concept as hell? Why did Robert Johnson turn away and face the wall when he was recording?

The traditional sources and biographies have no answers, and so it is in these lapses of factual evidence that we can speculate and theorise. The more we do so, the more we feel something like genuine empathy and kinship with our subject. We seek out and inhabit these dark recesses where knowledge and fact fall short of a full and comprehensive understanding. We own these spaces; it is as though, through our speculations and fantasies, we write ourselves into the story and can believe thereafter that we have actually become a part of it.

It is not criticism or appraisal; it is more like sneaking into the narrative. Whatever we may feel on the subject, Berrichon, Fowlie, Bonnefoy, Étiemble and Starkie are now as much a part of Rimbaud's legacy as the Rolling Stones are part of Robert Johnson's.

Much like the Fantasy Rimbaud on whom I have just turned my back – but sadly I suspect only literally – there is also a Fantasy Robert Johnson. I first encountered this particular version of the bluesman on the cover of that famous 1961 LP and on all its subsequent reissues. Entitled (optimistically or clairvoyantly) *The King of the Delta Blues Singers*, the artwork featured a painting of the singer as, at the time, no photographs were believed to exist. It is an iconic image, courtesy of the Columbia Records art department, of the figure of a seated solitary black man playing a guitar, evidently outdoors and viewed anonymously from above. For a long time, it was the only image to be had. It was, in effect, the equivalent of the Carjat photograph.

The picture, with its dominant red and brown tones, is immediate and powerful, stark and effective, but just like the statue of Rimbaud, it is also sentimentalised and hugely misleading. With his striped shirt, which could suggest either the plantation or penitentiary, this figure could be an illustration from a story by Mark Twain. Like the Vagabond Rimbaud, he is timeless and therefore both ancient and modern simultaneously.

And just like Rimbaud, the idea does not bear any close scrutiny. Johnson was actually born in 1911, which is later than the birth date of so many of the first generation of great jazz composers and performers: Duke Ellington, Bix Beiderbecke, Coleman Hawkins, Lester Young, Benny Goodman, etc. Now, be honest – it would be hard to imagine a quasi-medieval story about a deal with the devil attaching itself with such rigour to any of those musicians. Johnson's recording career coincided with the first great records made by the Count Basie Orchestra, but our perception of Johnson is, again, of a man outside or beyond history as we understand it. It is a resilient myth and one that can withstand all manner of challenges and counterarguments.

In the 1980s, a couple of photographs of Johnson were published for the first time. One in particular shows him smiling and dapper in a hat and pinstriped suit, posing for a photographer in a Memphis studio. Here was the image of a man perfectly captured in his own time: confident, assured, living and breathing, and a quite remarkable contrast to a painting on an old LP cover. You could almost feel the disappointment. Yet the idea of Robert Johnson, the essence of the man approximated in that first illustration, remains fixed in the imaginations of so many. It sat with our sense of the music and it came with us to the place the music took us. It was our idea of the artist corresponding to our idea of his art. And for many of us, that is all we ever needed.

The relative obscurity and scattered first-hand recollections of the artist in this respect is a major factor. Our need for a clear, romantic scenario drives our theories, speculations and even the images we create for ourselves. That we thereafter paint pictures and sculpt monuments of those images is a fairly inevitable consequence.

'*Pardon, divin Seigneur, pardon!*'[11]

In so many words...

I suppose if one invests a certain amount of oneself in one's obsessions, then a revelation about that obsession, however trivial, is ultimately a revelation on a personal level. But I don't want to think about that. I cross the road and, for the sake of something to do, I look at the river for five minutes.

I force my mind to concentrate on the small boats on the opposite bank. Maybe this is just another emotional construct, but several writers refer to Rimbaud bunking off school on summer days and borrowing a boat – just like, I imagine, the ones I am currently staring at. He would climb on board, push it away from the bank and lie on his back, gazing at the sky as the boat drifted silently on gentle, sunlit currents. For many years, I could picture myself in this boat so clearly that I could smell the

---

11   Forgive me, divine Lord, forgive me!

damp wood and hear the crickets. It is too tempting to imagine that, during one of these little excursions, he began to formulate the ideas behind 'Le Bateau Ivre'; that boat too drifted without any human control or authority.

Boats always seemed to feature in Rimbaud's life. There were the actual physical boats, of course: the means of flight and escape, always further and faster – the boats that took him to England initially and then to Africa later. Then there were the symbolic, metaphysical boats, such as 'Le Bateau Ivre', of course. And right at the end of his life, there was the 'Aphinar'.

On the actual day before he died, in fact, Rimbaud had dictated a letter to his sister Isabelle. Despite being so close to death, he was determined to return to Africa and continue his work there; his letter makes these intentions quite clear. It is practical, dogmatic and very much the voice of Merchant Rimbaud.

The letter is addressed to the director of Messageries Maritimes, and it enquires, ostensibly, about the current state of his account with the company. It also lists a number of lots of tusks and, in places, gives the impression of being a shipping manifest. It is a short letter of just over two paragraphs, and it trails off without a formal conclusion. What has always interested me is the reference to 'Aphinar'. From the context of his letter, this would seem to be the name of a place or even a shipping line. As he refers to being 'carried aboard' it is even possible he is alluding to a specific boat. The word is used twice, and this consistency alone suggests he was at least clear about the word in his own mind.

But the word doesn't exist, and no company, ship, place or anything has ever been known by that name. He was delirious and confused, of course, and Isabelle might have misheard the word (the Arab word for lighthouse is vaguely similar). But I'm not convinced by this. I think that, as the sheer imminent inevitably of his own demise hastened upon him, he did what he had done as a teenager two decades previously. He took solace in planning his escape. The older Rimbaud was still relying on the image of the boat as a transitional metaphor of being unmoored and free, drifting from one plane to the next.

Quintessentially, I think the 'Aphinar' was just another drunken boat.

Perhaps, in his final hours, he returned to his first departure point: going back to Charleville, to this dusty bank here and the old windmill. Perhaps, for one last time, he simply attempted to connect with the boy, the poet, whose existence he had denied for so many years. It's probably once again little more than a fantasy, but it unquestionably suits the same well-established narrative.

However, I feel as though I've had enough of such diversions for the time being, and at a slightly increased pace, I begin to walk back towards the centre of the town. There are other places I need to see, but for now, I feel most strongly that I might benefit from doing something as mundane as visiting a supermarket and buying a couple of bottles of water.

It is not long before I start thinking about Robert Johnson again and wondering why I am not currently somewhere in Mississippi, trying to make some sort of connection to something. Money might be a factor, of course, but the hold he has over me is less potent nowadays. An interest, an enthusiasm, a passion and an obsession – it really just comes down to a question of degree. Or how we feel about the person who is actually doing the obsessing. I used to think such focussed, single-minded idolatry was something predominantly male and vaguely connected to a person's rites of passage. I now doubt that this is the case, and I strongly suspect that, regardless of whether it's books or music or football, such passions are simply a convenient screen behind which boys and men *collect things*.

And there is very little joy in this realisation.

Middle age seems to bring with it what might be fondly regarded as the equivalent to these earlier rites of passage, only it seems to happen in reverse. Consequently, shame is just another one of those grand, abstract things that, without ceremony, removes itself from our lives at some point. When I first heard the term 'the Age of Anxiety', I was probably in my late teens and I think I contrived to miss the point entirely. I actually managed to convince myself that the expression was a reference to adolescence and the terrible horrors of puberty. That the Age of Anxiety might refer to a period in time, a determined epoch, never occurred to me.

Therefore, in my view, the Age of Anxiety was just something else that was summarised and articulated best by Rimbaud, as that wondrous, unimpeachable proto-teenager for all times.

But every age, every generation, is an Age of Anxiety. A battleground between new and old ideas, with the dreadful uncertainty that trails in its wake. Closely related, if not directly consequential, is the strong suspicion that those times we could regard as our Golden Age have now passed. The Golden Age is when TV and music were better, children were safer, and everything revealed itself in a manner I understood. It was the era of such marvellous certainties…

For the time being, Charleville, Rimbaud and Robert Johnson are going to have to function as my certainties.

I reach La Place Ducale again, and within a matter of minutes, I have found a branch of Carrefour City. As I approach, I notice a woman whose age, at first fleeting glance, I would put somewhere vaguely between thirty and forty sitting next to the entrance.

She makes eye contact and holds her hand out towards me. '*Monsieur?*' she says, her face animated and smiling.

For a moment, I ignore her gesture and, instead, I simply look at the expression on her face, marvelling in its complex vitality, like a man who has spent far too long conversing with monuments.

5. CHARITY

In several of the more reliable contemporary accounts of Rimbaud's first months in Paris with Verlaine, after that fateful first meeting at Rue Nicolet, references are made all too frequently to the younger poet's anti-social behaviour and speech.

'*Merde!*'

There are also stories that border on the criminal or simply violent. Rimbaud wrecked rooms, regularly sold furniture belonging to the people he stayed with and, famously, attacked Carjat with a sword. Some of these more extreme incidents have slightly dubious provenance, and if not wholly invented, then they are – at the very least – exaggerated. Indeed, their source can often be traced back to those, such as Verlaine's in-laws, whose reliability as impartial witnesses could never be wholly guaranteed. However, there is little doubt that Rimbaud seemed to permanently delight in provoking reactions and antagonising the bourgeoisie whenever possible.

There are precious few reminiscences that portray him in anything approaching a positive light, yet there remain one or two scattered references to him offering help and assistance to the homeless people he encountered sleeping rough in doorways and on the streets of Paris. These acts of genuine compassion confound the popular conception of Rimbaud, who is so often portrayed as something savage and amoral. Perhaps he felt a greater kinship with destitute and vagrants than he ever did with those he encountered at poetry readings. Perhaps he saw in them an older version of himself, eschewing all connections with conventional society for the sake of some sense of personal purity.

All I know is that, somehow, all this played its part in my awkward failure just now to offer that lady some money. I recalled the stories about Rimbaud, I questioned his motives and then swiftly started questioning my own. Then my mouth suddenly felt dry, my arms and my instincts paralysed, and I found myself darting into the relative sanctuary of the supermarket.

But aside from meanness and moral cowardice, my failure to respond in any vaguely empathetic manner left me feeling stupid rather than simply ill-mannered. Beyond that, it also highlighted one of the main flaws with the original theme of my book. A man, probably someone very like myself, revisits Charleville to reflect upon his own life. He re-examines his lasting fascination with the poet as a means of achieving something like self-discovery.

'Je est un autre.'

Translated usually as 'I is another' or, more awkwardly, as 'I is somebody else', this is another often-quoted phrase that is present in both the Lettres du Voyant. Widely discussed and endlessly reinterpreted, the expression suggests Rimbaud felt that strict definitions of mind and consciousness were illusory. Indeed, he believed a true poet (the *voyant*) should be sufficiently detached from his own thought processes to simply witness and record objectively what occurs. An understanding of this dichotomy and the consequences of such a radical shift in personal identity from the internal to the external is essential in any study of Rimbaud.

So the idea was initially to explore Rimbaud's work through a semi-autobiographical story of a man's lifelong interest in the poet. How every aspect of his adult life up to that point had been to a lesser or greater extent influenced by his obsession. My own (*je*) initial ideas were all developed around the theme of demonstrating how deeply Rimbaud had wormed his way into my fictional character's (*un autre's*) psyche. Even the inevitable flaws in this man's personality or lapses in judgement – and, indeed, the validity of the project itself – would be seen as echoes of the relative failures and weaknesses in Rimbaud's own character.

Having quickly abandoned the idea of a confession – a homage maybe, in the approximate manner of *Une Saison en Enfer* – I admit I have been struggling with the overall tone of the piece.

'It's not you, Rimbe, it's me...'

And I realise that I have just said this out loud.

A few people in the aisle for bottled waters and soft drinks turn towards me, and I smile and shuffle away as quickly as I can. Abruptly, I begin to feel hot, my hands are damp and my mouth is dry again; I feel slightly dizzy, and focussing on the first nearby thing I can see, I concentrate on the illustration on a cereal box to orientate myself as my brain races after an idea. It's chasing Rimbaud, of course; it's always Rimbaud.

But I will never catch him now.

'*L'homme aux semelles de vent.*'[12]

It is far too late; I can only watch him from a distance. I accept that now. Besides, it's not Rimbaud; no, it's not. It should always be Arthur Rimbaud; that is the name of a person, someone of bones and flesh, just like the rest of us – not a single-word myth. No, no, it's *Arthur* Rimbaud – the name of a man who lived and ate and slept and pissed and shat, just like everyone

---

12   The man with the wind at his heels.

else. A normal name, like Arthur Conley, Arthur Askey, Arthur Conan-Doyle, Arthur Scargill, King Arthur...

And I don't accept such narrow definitions of charity either. I shall go back and see the lady outside. Of course I will; I will do it immediately. I will give her all the money in my wallet! But I will do so out of decency, courtesy and even old-time chivalry. I smile to myself at the word as it makes me think of Sir Lancelot, King Arthur... King *Arthur*!

There is a rushing sound, crashing waves, a subway train – a hissing, sibilant brilliant sound that feels both around and inside me at the same time. Everything now converges in my head. Everything flows and compresses itself into a single tiny point, a microscopic moment in the infinity of all things – a living, pulsing heartbeat. I have no choice now, only the consequences of ancient actions...

With little warning or ceremony, it is now the New Theatre in Cardiff and the local Operatic and Dramatic Society is putting on a production of *Camelot*. Although it is an amateur company, it is a fine and lavish production, which has received generally favourable notices and is playing to nearly full houses most evenings. The actor playing King Arthur has been singled out particularly for his performance. Also mentioned in one review is the young boy who plays Sir Tom Mallory. OK, I admit that I know this because, of course, that young boy in question is the eight-year-old me.

Anyone familiar with the piece might well recall the final scene that occurs just before Arthur's last battle, during which he knows he will perish along with all the glory and the ideals of Camelot. Alone, he reflects upon the situation, and as he faces the inevitable, he is interrupted by a young boy, Tom Mallory. It is a wholly allegorical scene, as the historically dubious Arthur and Sir Thomas, who is the author of *Le Morte d'Arthur*, lived approximately 900 years apart. Yet, the scene is, generally speaking, an effective one. The two characters talk, and during their exchange, Arthur convinces the young Sir Thomas that he must document what happened at Camelot to ensure it will never fade from history. Their achievements would have been for nothing, King Arthur insists, if not recorded and passed on. Sir Thomas promises the king that he will do this, and Arthur is then fully prepared to meet his fate. The boy – and, yes, that would be me – runs off, and the curtain comes down.

I still have a black-and-white picture somewhere of me in my costume – which was hot and quite itchy, as I recall – grinning my very finest approximation of a showbiz smile. But having the director of the show explaining the purpose of the allegory to me and why it was the significant closing scene resonated with me at that age and has always remained with me. As a motif, it has turned up in my life many times: the sense of moving forwards, taking with you only the things that matter and ensuring you leave nothing worthwhile behind as it can never be replaced. I have failed in this at times and have always regretted it.

I hear its traces and echoes whenever I find myself talking about Rimbaud for any length of time. I sense the ghost of Sir Thomas Mallory. I think about the fear that what we judge to be our best achievements and greatest creations will amount to nothing unless they are recorded, celebrated and made pertinent for all time. That was Arthur's fear in that final scene in *Camelot* and maybe a tiny part of me playing Mallory has never left me. Is this another reason why I'm here in Charleville, desperately attempting to align myself with something I still consider relevant and permanent?

The panic passes. I open my eyes and reacquaint myself quickly with the familiar world of cereals, energy bars and biscuits, and for a moment or two, I simply delight in the mundanity, beauty and utter perfection of it all. Shortly afterwards, I leave the store without buying anything and return to the lady outside.

She looks up at me and with a very slight incline of her head, she smiles again. '*Monsieur?*' Her tone is warm and it teeters almost on the conversational; it is a greeting rather than an entreaty or a request.

I smile back and say nothing. Then I reach into my pocket and pull out a handful of notes. I think about handing them all over to her, but I worry that such a gesture might well be misinterpreted. So I instead offer a couple of five-euro notes and a few loose coins.

Her eyes widen; they are hazel to green and spark with fire and a curious intelligence. '*Monsieur?*' she asks, as though she needs me to somehow confirm the transaction.

'*Pour vous,*' I say, attempting a grin that might be broadly considered wholesome.

She smiles again. 'Thank you, *monsieur*; you are extremely kind.'

'Oh.' Startled, I exclaim, 'You're English?'

She shakes her head and pouts. 'No, *monsieur*. Look at me; I am clearly French.'

I take a small instinctive step backwards. 'But your English is impeccable; it's perfect.'

'Well,' she says through a sigh, 'for the benefit of your story, wouldn't it be a lot easier if I just spoke English?'

I consider her remark for a few moments. 'Well, there's the whole issue of authenticity, obviously, for one thing. This is Charleville; this is about as fucking French as it gets! And besides...'

'Besides what, *monsieur*?'

'Well, it does feel like a bit of a cop-out.'

'Surely, it's a simple matter of comprehension; you can't assume everyone can speak French! That's ridiculous! You'll make your story really difficult to follow if you constantly have to react or comment in English to what has been said by one of your characters in French.'

I think for a moment, conscious suddenly that I am being lectured on prose style by a lady in noticeably reduced circumstances. 'But I did have a chat with the woman at the hotel earlier.' I say, adopting a slightly defensive tone. 'That worked out OK, I think.'

She exhales loudly. 'But, *monsieur*, that was just mainly pleasantries, wasn't it? *Bonjour* and *merci* and blah, blah, blah. You weren't really talking about anything important, were you? Nothing remotely vital or of any relevance whatsoever to your overall narrative. Am I right?'

I do concede that her point is a valid one. I just thought it would be one I would ultimately resolve as I got into the actual process of writing.

But I'm not about to tell her that.

'And, *monsieur*, please don't tell me you were planning on having conversations where *ze* people, *zey* talk like *ziss* all the time, just to appeal to your distorted notions of regional authenticity. That would be just awful beyond words!'

'Oh please. Credit me with some sense! I would never do something like that.' I reply, hoping she doesn't notice the total absence of conviction or authority in my voice.

'You're the writer, monsieur; maybe you could say I was an au pair in *Meealton Keeenes* or somewhere like that. You'll think of something.'

'Yeah, I'll think about it…'

I shake my head, and we fall into silence for a few seconds.

Then she asks suddenly, 'So what should I call you, *monsieur*?'

'Henry Miller,' I snap back dryly.

She smiles indulgently. 'Very funny.'

I smile back. 'All right, sorry.' I tell her my real name.

'Then, I am very pleased to meet you. My name is Suzanne; Suzanne Autry. But everyone calls me Anne.'

'Really? I see. So, basically you're known as Anne Autry?'

'Yes. How do you do?' With an implied, suggestive grace, she offers me her hand.

Awkwardly, I take it and look at her with suspicion. 'Anne Autry? Seriously? For fuck's sake! Isn't that a bit clumsy? Even for me? I mean, come on now, Anne Autry? *Un autre?* You are kidding, right? It's like I'm not even trying any more!'

She bristles at this. 'It is my name, Monsieur Marc; I'm sorry if it upsets you.'

'Shit. No, I'm sorry; I really don't mean to sound rude or anything. I'm just wondering if the whole idea might be a little crude and overly obvious.'

At this point, not particularly wishing to continue any further with this line of conversation, I reach into my pocket, pull out another couple of ten-euro notes and hand them to her. 'Here,' I say, 'Take this; you've been really very helpful.'

'Thank you. But there's something else as well. You know that bit you did just now about Thomas Mallory?'

'Um… Yeah. What of it?'

'Well, surely you must be aware you wrote something very similar about him in one of your other novels.'

I say nothing.

'Oh, come on; you can't have forgotten.'

I only very dimly recall the passage to which she is referring. 'I think,' I say, pausing to gather my thoughts, 'that it was used in an entirely different context.'

'Oh, *monsieur*, I don't think that's entirely true.'

'Well, it's just a recurring motif then, isn't it?' I offer in casual desperation.

No, it's not; it's just lazy. Like you can no longer be bothered to come up with fresh ideas…'

Objective re-evaluation seems no longer available as an option, and I hear myself blurting out in defensive, hurried tones, 'Well, it's not as though anybody actually read the bloody thing anyway!'

'That, *monsieur*, is hardly the point, is it?' she says, evidently delighting in her conversational advantage. She then adds in predictably magnanimous tones, 'Besides, it had one or two good reviews, as I recall.'

Her voice now fades in the gentle breeze that plays around the perimeters of the warm afternoon as I turn to walk slowly back towards La Place Ducale.

For some reason, I am recalling that somewhere in the Bible, there's a line that I always thought could have sat quite well in *Une Saison en Enfer*. It is something to the effect of old men dreaming dreams and young men seeing visions.

Whilst, I presume, middle-aged men are doomed to wander the earth permanently, mired in confusion, uncertainty and doubt.

6. ORPHANS

Avenue Charles Boutet rises at a very slight gradient as it heads west from La Place Ducale. Given the slight over-opulence of the square, there is something about the avenue that strikes a contrasting and possibly welcome note of solid unpretentiousness.

As I walk and wait for the dozing, dusty, silent afternoon to exhale once again, I find that I am taking comfort in the regular sound of my own footsteps, like some distantly recalled ancient heartbeat. I'm measuring my stride now, falling into a rapid but even on-beat, off-beat – Stax-steady.

Boom, tack…

Regular.

Tack, boom…

Constant.

Somewhere on this avenue, I am certain, there will always be the priests, the four cantors, the eight choirboys, the beadle, the undertaker, the bell ringer, the grave-digger and the twenty orphan girls with candles. There will always be the richly draped hearse, the black plumes on the horses' heads and, at the rear there will always be Madame Rimbaud and her daughter Isabelle, as they follow the funeral procession of their respective son and brother. The date is 14th November 1891, and the whole ceremony has been arranged by Madame Rimbaud in a matter of hours.

The only mourners that day will be her and her daughter. Presumably, this is the method by which she can ensure that the reputation of her son will remain untarnished by any association with what she doubtless regards as undesirable elements. So no Verlaine, no Delahaye, no Izambard, no Germain Nouveau and so on.

At the highest point on Avenue Charles Boutet, where I now find myself, one reaches the gates to Charleville Cemetery, and it was here Rimbaud was buried on that November morning. I imagine it was a bleak, cold, wretched day with every detail of the ceremony forensically scrutinised by the ever-vigilant Madame Rimbaud, but I have no way of knowing. What we do know is that nine years after he was buried, Madame Rimbaud had the body exhumed and reburied in a more grandiose and rather pretentious family plot. This is where he remains to this day, alongside his sister Vitalie, who died in 1875. The inscription on the white marble is almost deliberately stark, with the gold lettering listing only his name, his age when he died and the actual date of his death. This information is written above the simple entreaty to pray for him: 'Priez pour lui.'

A similar plea, I notice, is also written on his sister's headstone. Although I confess it's only today that I notice this for the first time. Obviously, I visited the grave on my first trip twenty years ago, and it remains one of the absolutely essential destinations for the Rimbaud pilgrim. Dating from approximately the same period as the first statue in La Place de la Gare, it does again seem to exemplify the well-established conflict between our perception of Rimbaud as a perennial vagabond poet and how his mother and the general citizenry of Charleville chose to represent his life.

So here I am again, and no, I don't feel any less annoyed by his final resting place. It's a ghastly thing to behold. It is a blunt denial and rebuttal of every idea I ever had about the poet. This is the nearest I will ever physically come to Rimbaud. His dust, his bones and his DNA are less than a metre away from me, but the reality is that I have never been further away from any sense of him.

'Qu'est mon néant...?'[13]

Little seems changed in twenty years, although I notice there is now an unusual, rather ornate structure opposite the grave. I wander over to inspect it more closely. It seems part monument, part installation and part folly, and I must admit I find it a little confusing. With its impressive wingspan and radiating sun motif, I suppose my initial impression is of something ceremonial and ritualistic connected to ancient Aztec or Native American culture. But on closer inspection, it is actually little more than a functioning letter box! One that has been installed specifically for anyone who wishes to write a postcard or a letter to Rimbaud. It's a slightly bizarre addition to the cemetery, and it bisects the general solemnity of the place. It actually makes me feel uneasy, and to my mind, it suggests something that one might encounter in Graceland. In its mitigation, it might just be that the groundsmen had grown weary of removing personal mementos, fan mail and bad poems from the actual tomb itself, and this was simply a practical idea that would alleviate the problem.

I reach in my pocket for my phone, and for a moment, I think about taking a photograph. But this is another version of Rimbaud, another one of his *autres* and even more remote to me than the man in the earth behind me. I put my phone back in my jacket, turn and wander over to the grave again.

'Qu'est mon néant, auprès de la stupeur qui vous attend?'[14]

13   What is my nothingness...?
14   What is my nothingness, compared to the stupor that awaits you?

On noticing something else I am reasonably certain was not here on my previous visit, my attention is now drawn to the new dark marble headstone in the adjacent plot to Rimbaud's immediate right as I look at him. I lean over, read the inscription and discover that Rimbaud has found his eternal rest alongside a certain Monsieur Hulot.

I smile at this. I stop myself, and then I smile again.

I offer this entirely as a personal observation, and it should be in no way regarded as a criticism, but the study of Rimbaud generally leaves very little room for levity. There is so little humour in Rimbaud, dark or otherwise. So the idea of Jacques Tati's most famous comic creation barging into our narrative is possibly not an appealing one. Rimbaud took himself and his art extremely seriously, and anyone who studies him invariably follows his lead. Sometimes, I have wondered if the natural, self-righteous truculence of adolescence was a contributing factor to the tone of his work, but I can't even half-convince myself of this if I'm honest. Rimbaud was totally committed to his art and the ideology that went with it. Of that, there is no question, but it was a solemn, almost sombre aesthetic and, aside from the odd scatological reference, there are no moments of comedic respite in Rimbaud.

Actually, this could be considered a curious aspect of a writer who is universally regarded as one of the great precursors of modernism and the avant-garde. The American writer Roger Shattuck isolated the four dominant traits of modernity in the years between 1885 and 1914, which are these: allusions to childhood, references to dreams and hallucinations, a sense of ambiguity, and the incorporation of humour and absurdity. One only has to think of the works of Jarry or Duchamp and these qualities become self-evident.

So what then of Rimbaud?

Of him as the great standard-bearer of new literature writing a mere decade earlier?

I can think of no single example of the latter category in his work. As potent a denial of literature as anything in *Une Saison en Enfer*, his final documented poem – a few lines about soldiers farting – in a letter from October 1875 is the only thing that springs to mind.

I stare at his tomb because I don't seem able to stare at anything else at this moment. Instinctively, I shake my head, although more in resignation than in sadness. And the moral is – assuming, of course, that there is a moral – if you choose to mock bourgeois convention, just be aware that it will outlive you and, one day, it will just fucking mock you right back.

In fatuous conclusion, I exhale loudly and allow my mind to drift back now to the day of the funeral, and I think of Madame Rimbaud, whose willpower, stoic single-mindedness and overwhelming strength of personality were inherited but never surpassed by her eldest son. Sadly, the more you delve into Rimbaud's world, the more you are forced to confront the very strong possibility that the key relationship in his life remained the one he had with his mother. Despite its literary significance and the scandal that attended it, his association with Verlaine lasted less than four years. Whereas the correspondence he maintained with his family during the years following his abandonment of poetry reveal how he remained desperate to prove himself a worthy son in his mother's eyes.

The cold, aloof, unemotional tone of these letters, during which he frequently catalogues the hostility of his environment and the successes of his business enterprises, are sadly a fitting tribute to the influence of his mother. The letters that he wrote home from Africa from 1875 up until his death in 1891 remain problematic to many scholars, critics, biographers and the rest of us ordinary fans. Beyond being another *autre*, this is a Rimbaud whose deeds we have to somehow convert into reaction, denial or rebellion (God forbid), but most of all, we must always ensure that his lifetime's endeavours somehow remain a direct *consequence* of his earlier literary ambitions.

Perhaps the most renowned of these letters was written in May 1883, twelve years after the *Lettres du Voyant*, and it would be difficult to imagine a starker or more brutal rebuttal of his earlier aims. He whines and complains about his life, his job and money. He suggests his sister should get married if a well-educated man shows an interest. Then he bemoans the fact that he had never married and, furthermore, regrets that he hadn't fathered a son he could personally educate so that the boy could one day become a renowned engineer, *'un ingénieur renommé'*. It's a depressing read for anyone with a fixed image in their mind of the eternally damned poet, but the overall tone is suggestive. This is Rimbaud writing about his hardships in terms his mother would understand. In this and so many of his other letters of the same period, he seems desperate to present himself as an honourable, hard-working man and a person of principle and consequence. A businessman and a son that a mother might appreciate, support and perhaps, given time, even love.

Ironically, during these eighteen years, he had also – intentionally or otherwise – turned himself into a citizen worthy of respect back here in his loathed hometown.

A very early biographer of Rimbaud, writing a year or two even before Starkie, refreshingly had no difficulty accommodating the duality between Poet Rimbaud and Businessman Rimbaud. He saw both as manifestations of the same drive and ambition. Rimbaud didn't want to be a successful poet; Rimbaud wanted to revolutionise the whole concept of literature. Similarly, in Africa, he intended to amass a personal fortune, and given the magnitude and scope of his goals in this respect, it also appeared that he harboured aspirations to build his own empire. Thus, the writer concludes both episodes signify a lust for power and that, ultimately, the story of Rimbaud is the story of thwarted ambition.

This is not a view that is widely held nowadays, but the book goes on to list in some detail the negative personality traits of Madame Rimbaud, so in that respect, it upholds the traditional narrative. Hard, close-minded, distant, snobbish and ill-educated – the poor old girl doesn't stand a chance. In fairness, she was very possibly all of those things at one time or another. But I don't imagine being a single mother in a place like Charleville – abandoned by her husband, the father of her four children – can have been easy for her, and in fact, such an event might have dented most people's sense of humour.

Childhood is a series of small cruelties.

Everyone discovers that.

Eventually.

So is this, then, to be my subtext – the re-evaluation of the role of a mother in the life of a writer or, indeed, a self-defining failed writer or ex-writer? I'm not sure if this is a subject I would wish to explore. True, it seems pertinent to my situation, but I worry it might be a little overly obvious, all things considered. Besides, the recently bereaved are notoriously tedious narrators. It's one of their curiously unappealing quirks. They also grant themselves far too much licence and recognise no moral or social constraint on any aspect of their behaviour. This temptation to lapse into uninhibited self-gratification as a kind of emotional anaesthetic is, I admit, rarely less than appealing: 'Oh, I did this terrible thing, but my mummy died, and I'm an orphan, you see...'

The mythology of bereavement is that it is in some way a process: something indicative of motion, a moving away from a particular point in time. But nothing moves, nothing changes and nothing slowly returns to normal; there's no timetable, no clock or calendar that makes sense any more. You mistrust your own emotions, you mistrust your own memories, and you even begin to doubt your own instincts.

Yes, absolutely, whilst we are on the subject, *'Je est un autre.'*

'It was interesting, I always thought,' says a considered voice behind me, 'that, in his letters, he never addresses his family by name and only calls them "my dear friends" ("*mes chers amis*"). This always struck me as being curiously detached and strangely formal.'

I turn around and I am surprised to see Madame Autry now standing in the shade of a cypress tree, next to the ornate ceremonial postbox.

'*Madame?*' I say cautiously.

She inclines her head and smiles. 'Monsieur Marc.'

'How did…? I mean…' I gesture with my thumb at some vague, indeterminate location over my right shoulder.

'I followed you, *monsieur*. I was bored.'

I don't know what I was expecting her to say, but her answer surprises me. Although I should concede that the part of me that is flattered significantly outweighs the part that might feel any slight sense of alarm.

'I guessed you might be coming here. They usually do.'

'Sorry to be so obvious and predictable,' I say with a smile, silently acknowledging that something vague and undoubtedly nameless in some large, dark recess inside me has just eased very slightly at the sight of her.

'No, *monsieur*. I understand. Perfectly.' She begins to walk towards me. 'You must come here and try to feel something. Something important or significant. A connection, perhaps?' She shakes her head as though answering her own question. 'But there is nothing here: there is no beauty, no love, no poetry and no art, just that great fucking shadow that is cast over all of it.'

I mutter something under my breath, which – thankfully – she doesn't hear.

'You know, you should really think about leaving now, *monsieur*. I don't think it's the best place for you to be at this moment.'

I run my fingers across the stubble on my chin and offer her a lop-sided smile. 'Yeah. You know, you're probably right.'

She leans towards me and takes my arm 'Come on, *monsieur*, you can buy me a beer.'

The afternoon sun is still warm and I admit I find her suggestion a tempting one. I glance back briefly towards the tomb, and I feel a little annoyed and a little sad, but these seem to be my defining characteristics at the moment and may have little to do with the tomb itself.

So, I accompany Madame Autry, who is walking at a fairly rapid pace as she escorts me from the cemetery. Possibly, I like to think, out of a benevolent sense of duty, but realistically, it is perhaps that she simply craves alcohol.

'I find it all a bit sentimental, to be honest,' she says airily after a few moments, as we walk back along Avenue Charles Boutet.

'You find what sentimental, exactly?'

She shrugs. 'Emotional, then?'

'What?'

She scoffs and waves her free arm theatrically. 'All... all this, *monsieur*.'

Frowning, I make eye contact with her, but I say nothing.

'Rimbaud!' She invests the name with more world-weary derision than I would have imagined possible. 'I am so sick of him. Really, Monsieur Marc, it is a waste of your time. It is, for you, nostalgia and sentiment, I believe – and little else. It is not dignified, and it serves no purpose.'

Again, beyond a slight raising of my eyebrows, I can think of no suitable response.

'Nostalgia,' she continues, 'is a terrible illness. It is absolutely disgusting and nothing beyond... What would you say?' She pauses and looks directly into my eyes.

'Self-tourism!' she exclaims eventually.

'Yes, that's it,' she says, quite evidently delighted with the expression. 'And you can just see the fucking brochures, can't

55

you? "Come with us and spend an enchanting week exploring the sunny, unspoilt beaches of your inaccurately recalled adolescence! Delight in the convivial local atmosphere and charming ambience, which will fortunately be masking any traces of actual memory, together with any recollection of your loneliness, pain and utter misery..."

I shake my head and smile at her with something like genuine affection. 'Look, I assure you that is not the reason—'

She raises her hand to silence me. 'Please, *monsieur*, do not succumb; do not wallow. It is unbecoming in an intelligent gentleman such as you. Furthermore, and I can say this with absolute certainty, such a pointless indulgence would never have been tolerated by your Rimbaud. Not in a million years, *monsieur!*'

She grips my arm a little tighter than is possibly necessary, and we continue walking in silence.

7. Masks

In an attempt to distance myself from the focus of the immediate activity and craving a distraction, however fleeting, I focus first upon his moustache and then on his rather severe side-parting. In my mind, I find that I am able to convert him into a painting by Honoré Daumier: a vicious caricature of some humourless, cold, petty-minded official or bureaucrat, delighting in his capacity to refuse, obstruct or deny.

However, it does very little to alleviate the situation, and in actual fact, I quickly find myself wandering off topic and thinking about Madame Rimbaud again.

Meanwhile, the man whom I have made the unwitting focus of my attention remains stoically unmoved in any discernible way behind the counter – although I notice he is now shaking his head with even greater conviction, if such a thing were possible.

'*Non,*' he says, without appearing to actually move his mouth. '*Non!*'

Possibly prompted by a sense of humility, Madame Autry attempts a small smile at this point, but it is a hugely ambiguous and ill-conceived gesture – one that I imagine being hastily judged as evidence of her total self-absorption or, even worse, an implication of contempt and mockery. The man behind the counter would certainly seem to be thinking along those lines.

'You must leave now,' he says, pointing a particularly emphatic index finger towards the door.

He lapses into silence, but the finger remains fixed as permanent instruction and testimony.

In an attempt to distance myself very slightly from the drama being played out directly in front of me, one in which I would like to believe I was only involved tangentially, I turn my head and look around the bar at the other customers. Perhaps they might appreciate my Honoré Daumier reference? Perhaps they would recognise the comedic pertinence of such a correlation, identify with my situation, raise their glasses to me, pat me on the back and…

No, not today.

But here they all are again: the great-great-great-great grandchildren, with their beers, their regrets and a big-screen TV – lost once again in themselves and in the terrible hopelessness of a long, sleepy summer afternoon.

'Leave please. You too, *monsieur*.'

Shit!

I catch his eye and reach inside my jacket for my wallet. 'Now, look, can't we just settle this?' I open my wallet and take out a credit card in what I hope is a universally recognised gesture. 'If you just tell me how much the lady owes you, I'd be happy to settle up.'

He shakes his head again. 'No, *monsieur*, it is not just the money she owes me. Although that is part of it, of course. Look around you; I have all kinds of people in here! But I will not serve *her*!' He adds a curious emphasis to the word, but his point is clear enough. 'This lady is too disruptive, she drinks far too much, and she shouts and upsets my other customers. She is a troublemaker, and she is not welcome here. She is barred, and she also knows she is barred.'

I glance over at Madame Autry, who, pouting theatrically, shrugs her shoulders and turns her back to me.

The man behind the bar sees this and gestures silently in triumph, as though his point has just been proved beyond any shadow of a doubt.

Meanwhile, I notice that Monsieur Daumier is no longer present; he has put on his battered straw hat, packed up his easel and his brushes, and – without a backward glance – has wandered out into the street, seeking the long shadows of the afternoon sun.

I attempt and possibly overshoot the affable smile. 'OK, I take your point. But maybe you could just give her another chance? I will ensure that—'

'No, *monsieur*,' says the man, raising his voice. 'You must both leave now.'

I feel my arm being suddenly tugged as I'm led rapidly back through the bar and out of the door by Madame Autry.

'That man is a fucking idiot!' she declares.

The sentiment, although possibly predictable, is evidently heartfelt and requires no further comment from me.

'Fuck him and his shitty little bar,' she continues. 'My friends and I used to go there all the time, but never again!'

'Well, it seems you owe him some money.'

She frowns and exhales dramatically. 'It's a question of timing; it's just a cycle, a natural cycle. I owe him money and then I pay him back. It's as simple as that, and it's the way it has always been! But before I pay him back, I am this bad, terrible woman. After I pay him back, however, nobody – not him, not anyone – considers me a good or decent person particularly. It seems unfair.'

'If you say so,' I say absently, not wishing to endorse or antagonise in any way. Although if I am honest, I do find her whole take on the issue a tad sulky and adolescent.

'Anyway, this bad, terrible woman still wants a beer!'

I propose that we try the Bar de l'Univers, but she shakes her head. Instead, she suggests we buy a six pack from the supermarket and find a quiet bench near the river. She points out that it might be a little cooler there, and by this point in the day, I'm not inclined to offer her any alternative.

'After you, *madame...*' I say, gesturing vaguely.

We return to the branch of Carrefour City where I had encountered her for the first time a couple of hours previously. We disagree about the brand, obviously, but we settle eventually on her choice.

As we walk back towards the Le Place Ducale and she discusses in fairly tedious detail the alcoholic content of the various imported beers that were available in the supermarket, I catch myself once again sneaking the odd glance at my companion.

What I had originally thought to be evidence of decay or just general dissipation is nothing of the kind; it was simply a general lack of interest in such things. She seemed unfettered and unbound by orthodox ideas of beauty; her face mocked you and dared you to pass judgement or appraisal, as if it were so far beyond the realm of all established feeble, aesthetic evaluations. Events and circumstances had left their traces, but this could not fully disguise or obscure an essential quiet grace. It seemed to me – in that brief, stolen glimpse – that her face had somehow evolved to coexist with the idea of beauty; it referenced it without being directly or conventionally beautiful. It was as though she were beyond it and it had not yet caught up with her.

This entire concept was best illuminated by the cipher I believed might be decoded the more I maintained my fleeting covert surveillance of her features.

In doing so, I attempt to avoid making direct eye contact. Even from the comparatively short time I had known her, I still feel there is something private and haunted just about discernible behind her eyes. They challenged you, lured you and tempted you to seek out the drama of ancient events, as though every tear that had ever been shed had etched an enduring marker or trail to be discovered, interpreted or translated. In unguarded moments, of which there were precious few, I could also determine so easily a frail, terrible honesty; the eyes of one who could see no virtue or purpose in deception…

But like anything in Rimbaud, any simple judgement was deceptive, and any momentary revelation would only involve me in further enquiry and even more doubt and confusion. In my experience, a mask is often simply a device that successfully obscures another mask.

Yet all these were issues that remained quite clearly of little or no concern to her.

Even beyond this, her face reflected, second by second, her whole existential human experience; constantly animated, alive and receptive to everything around her, it never seemed to me to be in repose, even for a moment. Her eyes darted and her mouth changed expression virtually constantly – from the practised sneer to a sudden suggestion of beatific wonder and all the possible mortal variations in between. It was difficult sometimes to ascertain precisely why she would suddenly melt into the warmest of smiles. Had she just heard or seen something I'd missed? Was this some pleasing memory she was revisiting? Either way, it was private and exclusive, and nobody else would ever be invited.

I knew in those stolen few seconds what I would always envy the most about her.

It was simply that she seemed so much more alive than I had ever been.

'Pah!' The sound of her voice abruptly explodes into my reverie. 'They probably treated your Rimbaud no better in his day,' she adds loftily, 'but now they put up idiotic monuments and statues in his honour.'

I smile with all the practised conviction of an innocently guilty schoolboy. 'That's probably very true,' I say in ambitiously level tones. 'And of course…' I take a breath, and I hate myself and my entire stupid life so much for saying, 'of course,' but I blunder on regardless. 'That's exactly the sort of thing he would have despised.'

'Exactly, *monsieur.*'

We turn into the Rue Moulin, and she gestures extravagantly towards the Musée Rimbaud, which is clearly visible now at the end of the road. 'I mean, have you seen that new installations by the museum down there? That thing with all those fucking chairs?'

The work to which she is referring dates from 2011 and consists of eighteen stainless-steel chairs arranged along the pavement by the river adjacent to the museum. Each chair, which is individually designed and fashioned, features a quote from Rimbaud alongside a quote from a contemporary French-speaking poet. I had read about it, but I had deliberately avoided it earlier, following my awkward encounter with the new statue.

'I saw it at a distance a little while ago,' I answer after a considered pause, 'but not actually up close.'

'Well,' she states, immediately warming to her topic, 'you can read the poem or you can sit on it. Really, is that the message? You can be transported by the words of our wonderful boy-poet and all his cronies, or you can just stick your arse on them! Seriously, now, I'm telling you that really is something Rimbaud would have loved!'

'Maybe that's the point,' I suggest half-heartedly, but she ignores me and breaks into a mocking chuckle.

'Idiots,' she concludes with sneer. 'Everything about this place is just ridiculous.'

At the bottom of Rue Moulin, we turn right into Quai Jean Charcot to avoid the offending items and make our way to the gentle slopes of the river bank adjacent to the Musée Rimbaud.

We eventually find a bench somewhere fairly cool and shaded near the water's edge, and we sit down. To be strictly accurate, I sit down on the bench and she sits down cross-legged on the grass in front of me.

'Well, here's to Rimbaud and to you, *monsieur*,' she says as she opens a beer and waves the can vaguely in my direction.

'Cheers,' I respond, as I tip the corner of my can against hers.

A couple stroll past us, arm in arm, and the man catches Madame Autry's eye and mutters something under his breath. They pick up their walking pace and move away quickly.

She exhales loudly and looks at me with a pained expression. Then she turns towards the retreating figure of the man. 'Yeah, you too, *monsieur*,' she says with a slightly exaggerated sneer, which I suspect might have been for my benefit.

'Friend of yours?' I suggest blankly.

'He's a fucking arsehole.'

I take a sip of my beer, which I find surprisingly strong, and muffle a sigh. I close my eyes for a moment and feel the sun on my eyelids.

'Do you have a fish tank, *monsieur*?'

I open my eyes all of a sudden. 'Do I have a what?'

'A fish tank, an aquarium?'

This was not a line of questioning I was expecting, and in truth, I can think no suitable reply. This, however, fails to deter her even slightly.

'My father, he had a freshwater fish tank when I was growing up, and he kept a few goldfish.' She smiles, and under different circumstances, I might have picked up a suggestion of wistfulness.

I stare at my beer can; I nod but say nothing.

'Have you heard of a fish called a pleco, *monsieur*?' she asks earnestly.

'No, I don't think so.'

'It is basically a fish that cleans your fish tank. It eats the algae and all the stuff that accumulates in the tank. They say it also eats the shit of the other fish. So you buy them in the pet store, and they keep your tank clean for you.'

'I see,' I say with the maximum interest I can muster for the subject.

'My father, he used to tell me that this was a perfect example of symbiotic evolution. How the species coexist in an ecosystem with one feeding off the waste of the other. Anyway, that man who just walked by, him...' She points. 'He calls me Madame Pleco.'

I make a face. 'That's not very nice.'

'I have been called worse, believe me. But for the rest of this afternoon, I shall be Madame Pleco, and I'm pleased to make your acquaintance.' She smiles lavishly for a few moments and then seems to weary of her own joke. 'But Rimbaud... he also always makes me think of the pleco fish. Engulfed and surrounded by the shit, the terrible, suffocating...'

'*Merde!*'

'Yes, the *merde* of his time, and yes, of course, his... *place.*' She gives the word predictable emphasis and gestures with her beer can in case the point was not being made clearly enough. 'But perhaps, you know, if you wallow in shit long enough, you eventually find something shining, divine and perfect; a sense of destiny or purpose; or simply the necessary willpower to overcome adversity... and all the rest of the shit...!'

Her voice trails off as though she is losing interest in the subject, whilst I find myself thinking about that line in 'Le Bateau Ivre' when the narrator regrets failing to show children '*ces poissons d'or, ces poissons chantants...*'[15]

Meanwhile, Madame Autry is suddenly animated once more. 'You know, it always used to bother me when I was little and my question to my father was always the same: so what eats the shit of the shit-eating fish?'

---

15   those golden fish, those singing fish...

I smile. 'I wonder how on earth the man coped living with such a profound young thing.'

She raises her eyebrows for a moment. 'Of course, you know that's what Verlaine used to call Rimbaud after they separated. Thing. He writes to mutual friends and asks if they have any news of Thing. It's a very strange, impersonal term, don't you think? Almost dehumanising in a way. But I suppose he was not a particularly happy person at the time.'

'Maybe, but there are times in everyone's life when, for sanity's sake, they need to keep a cold, emotional distance.'

She lets out a brief scornful chuckle. 'Ah, that great English need for objectivity and spiritual detachment! So how has that worked so far for you, Marc?'

'Well, Anne, now you're asking…'

I feel my cheeks redden, and I quickly attempt to change the subject. 'You know, he did actually sign an early letter to Izambard as "that heartless A. Rimbaud" and it's fair to say he exhibited a cold, ruthless ambition sometimes. I know some critics have attempted to read this as something akin to traditional adolescent self-absorption, but it's not the most convincing argument.'

My words, always as relevant and as substantial as dust, drift lazily and pointlessly in the afternoon haze to occupy the dwindling space between us.

'I admit it's not a side of his character that one would wish to dwell upon,' I say, as the world's greatest Rimbaud bore finally gets into his stride. 'But certainly, in his life – if not in his work – he does so often seem emotionally disconnected from the consequences of his actions.'

At this remark, her eyes narrow gradually as her face composes itself into an expression I had not hitherto observed. I can sense that she is looking at me now with a sort of quiet tolerance.

But, I am delighted to notice, not entirely without affection.

8. Timelines

I suppose this is the point in my narrative when I should address an issue that I have so far been attempting to circumvent. Although I can offer no real reason to account for why I would wish to avoid it. There was no planning involved, but beyond inadvertent oversight, I really can't explain it. Perhaps I have simply not wanted anyone to form the wrong idea.

So, the fact remains that, beyond my scrutiny of her facial features and approximating her age earlier, I have made very few comments on my companion's appearance. The circumstances under which we met may have led you to imagine that she might have the look of long-term homelessness: that ingrained patina of the streets, like one lost forever in the dirt of all our days – the kind that is absorbed into the bloodstream, the mind and, eventually, the soul.

This, however, would create an entirely inaccurate impression.

Being impartial, one could say Madame Autry looks a little unkempt maybe, but the whole effect suggests a certain intention on her part. Her hair appears dishevelled, but again,

I would hesitate to assume this was inadvertent. To my mind, it continues to imply a deliberate defiance, rather than a reduction in circumstances.

Today, she is wearing a large, striped T-shirt and what I assume are Lycra cycling shorts. On her feet, she wears a pair of ancient-yet-well-maintained high-end trainers. I suppose what I'm attempting to say is that she doesn't conform to my stereotypical idea of a beggar. Although a couple of hours previously, I had witnessed her doing precisely that. She confuses me in a strange, rather unfathomable way that actually draws me towards her. I want to learn her story.

Or perhaps I simply want to discover her secrets…

Meanwhile, we have not moved from our spot in the park, and I am listening to her talking about Rimbaud again.

'You – well, people like you – you are almost like those terrible parents you see sometimes: you overindulge him, make excuses for him and spout these huge claims on his behalf. Like he is some wild, supernatural entity, almost. You regard him as this unwitting artistic clairvoyant – someone who, without knowing it, was a punk, a communist, a beatnik, a surrealist, an atheist, and on and on. But basically, he is just some obscure outsider figure whom you have made personally responsible for everything in your stupid, white-male culture that you consider worthwhile…'

I pout quite theatrically at this final remark, but she doesn't seem to notice.

'If you look hard enough for it, you will always find what you are looking for. But to me, *monsieur*, next to, say, Baudelaire or Mallarme, your Rimbaud was always a minor poet, albeit one with a sort of toxic charisma that continues to fascinate people. And please don't fall for that "precursor of modernity" stuff either.'

My beer tastes warm and unpleasant now as I recall my thoughts a short while ago whilst I contemplated his headstone in the cemetery. 'Er... well, I'm not... you know, absolutely convinced...' I hear myself saying in a small voice.

'It doesn't work for me,' she states brusquely. 'I don't see the connection at all. It's just how you choose to construct your idiotic timelines! And you people are always very selective and creative with your timelines, I think. Personally, I believe his work sits more comfortably right at the end of the Romantic tradition and not part of the vanguard of modernism.'

I watch her as she takes a thoughtful, long sip of her beer before returning to her subject.

'If you don't believe me, ask yourself this: if you want to change the whole face of literature, why choose poetry as your means of expression? By Rimbaud's time, the significance of poetry was dwindling; it was no longer the medium of the masses. His era was the era of the novel. Even before he starts writing poetry, Flaubert and Zola have already published their most significant works. Indeed, you could quite easily argue that the novel was already the dominant literary art form by that time. Yet he decides he wants to change the world through poetry. It is madness! It would be something like, say, Picasso and Braque in 1905 attempting an artistic revolution through the medium of tapestry!' She smiles at her own allusion, and I wonder if she has used it before.

I reflect upon this for a moment. I always felt Picasso's modernity was significantly less combative and more inclusive. His reworkings of themes by Velasquez and Manet weren't a denial of their significance, but more a means by which they could be rebranded, updated and dragged along with the great surge of the avant-garde. Instead, cast outside their own epoch, Picasso ensures they are not of their time but for all time.

Rimbaud, by comparison, seems to have favoured the scorched earth approach.

Meanwhile, Madame Autry is still talking: 'You and your kind are too besotted with Rimbaud, and you can't think dispassionately. And I suppose, from your perspective, there is always this great romance about poetry, and therefore it follows that there is always a romance about poets, huh?'

I look at her face and search for and find the kindness in her eyes. 'Perhaps,' I say, 'he saw poetry as a more vital and spontaneous literary form, something visceral and immediate. Maybe he just saw himself in the spirit of the traditional outsider poet, like François Villon…'

She lets out a sudden, loud chuckle at this, which veers away from disdainful and teeters on cruel before settling on sardonic. 'Oh, *monsieur*! So the great forefather of the avant-garde models himself on a fucking fifteenth-century poet…'

'I didn't mean it like that…' I offer in suitably wounded tones.

'I know, I know…' She leans over and touches my knee.

As she does, I notice her long, tapering fingers for the first time. Their simple elegance at this precise moment seems unfitting or inappropriate, and I sense that, in some way, they are also mocking me. By comparison, I feel I am forever rooted in banality and quiet despair.

Madame Autry now stands up and brushes from her shorts the dust of the afternoon and our conversation. She takes a couple of steps and, after removing another beer from our carrier bag, sits down on the bench next to me.

'Now, you mentioned that blues singer Robert Johnson earlier, *monsieur*, did you not?'

Feeling less alarmed or even surprised than I might have previously, I turn towards her and nod. 'Yes, I did.'

'You see, I think you are right and your comparison is a fair one. He is another great enigmatic artist who is just about mysterious enough to bypass any definitive appraisal or a single overview. Like Rimbaud, his work has been endlessly picked over and discussed in what amounts to little more than a battle for personal ownership. Likewise, the man is exalted as the vast influence on this movement or that individual. But because something is not disprovable, it is not automatically a guarantee of veracity.'

I am, I confess, a little disappointed by this sudden shift in the conversation, but I say nothing for fear of interrupting her train of thought.

'And you know, like Rimbaud, he has been forced to occupy a place on a timeline that focuses on a single aspect and seriously oversimplifies his work... no, his art, I should say. For he was an artist in every sense. But for our convenience, we locate him at the start of a generation that runs through Muddy Waters, Elmore James, Howlin' Wolf and up to the likes of The White Stripes.'

I feel my shoulders tensing slightly. 'But he was a major influence on all those people. That is surely beyond question— '

'Yes, yes... but perhaps I could suggest another timeline for you? Robert Johnson wrote lyrics for songs with titles such as 'Love in Vain Blues' and 'Hellhound on My Trail', but these are not part of the traditional blues vernacular. They are a world away from the likes of 'Dust My Broom' and 'Rolling and Tumbling'. Actually, to me, the titles alone sound almost Elizabethan, and a number of the lyrics are genuinely extraordinary. Sometimes, there are aspects that almost remind me of Whitman. And speaking personally, I can never see words like 'Love in Vain' and not think of John Donne.'

I shake my head. 'So, let me get this right... rather than being a massive influence on blues music from the 1940s onwards, he is what? The last great Elizabethan poet?'

She wrinkles her nose and taps my knee again in a manner I tell myself is evidence only of her vague annoyance with me. 'No, Marc, don't be silly! I'm just attempting to show that any timeline is only ever subjective at best. It only shows a single aspect and can be a very simplistic approach to history. It's deceptive and manipulative. Actually, to be honest, it saddens me that we prefer our history to be so simple, like the simple choices between right and wrong, moral and immoral, and just and unjust. So we put Arthur Rimbaud in this box and Robert Johnson in a different box, and then we all feel safe and good about ourselves because we finally think we understand.'

I don't entirely agree with this, although it's possible I simply fear that her comments are aimed at me a little too directly. I feel there is a personal judgement implicit in her remarks, and I'd prefer not to be the person in question.

Seeking, then, to shift the subject fractionally away from me, I suggest that I could have used Robert Johnson as the basis for a book instead. 'After all,' I conclude, 'making a deal with the devil is possibly a little more dramatic and literary than simply having nits and pissing off Verlaine's in-laws.'

Madame Autry bristles at this remark or possibly just misses the implied sarcasm. 'No, you must write about Rimbaud; it is why you are in Charleville, surely?'

I say nothing, but I turn away and gaze for a moment through the trees to the small rowing boats moored on the opposite river bank. Boats that once drifted on impassive rivers and bathed in the poem of the sea; boats that once took me to Cyprus, to Aden and to Harare, but never allowed me to leave.

'The book,' I say slowly, 'if there ever is a book, is not really going to be about Rimbaud, or rather it would never be *solely* about Rimbaud.'

She looks puzzled. 'But then why would you come here? I mean out of all the places you could visit?'

Is this the moment I tell her, a relative stranger, about my crisis of identity when even the term was laughable when said out loud? Do I feel prepared to discuss my mother's death in March? Or how the current political climate makes me feel like my country has been invaded and I no longer understood the customs, the aspirations and the attitudes of my own generation? How I'd once armed myself against pain and despair by attempting to laugh at the absurdity and the stupidity of human cruelty? How that method was now failing me, no longer fit for purpose and worse than useless? Should I mention this constant sense of feeling abandoned, of growing rootlessness and the resulting desperate need for some level of certainty in my life? So, *madame*, here I am; I return to the sanity and the safety of my personal psychic departure lounge. I have returned to Rimbaud; I have returned to Charleville.

My companion now yawns in sympathy and straightens her back. 'If the key is Rimbaud, the key to Rimbaud is Charleville. You must trust me on that. It is here; it is all around you.'

'But Anne, it's not just about Rimbaud; it's about— '

She jumps to her feet and holds her hands up to silence me. 'No, *monsieur*, it is about pain – your pain. And you must put that pain onto the page. You must make it personal; let it pour out of you.' She shrugs her shoulders as though what she is saying is simply self-evident or else the matter is suddenly of little importance to her. 'I don't know if you're willing or wanting to do that, but I don't think you should worry about it being self-indulgent or boring; it would actually be quite the opposite.'

'So, what do you want? You want the love, suffering and madness, do you? *Amour, souffrance, folie?*'

She stifles a chuckle. 'Well, it worked for Rimbaud! Famously, it was once his path to enlightenment and to the unknowable. Actually, as you know, it was this precise theory that drove him to produce his most brilliant work. Why would you think that articulating your suffering or your pain would be any less valid or less significant?'

I concede she may possibly have a point, but for the moment, I decline to reply. In fact, for the first time that afternoon, I don't feel I have the authority or the confidence in my own ideas to contradict or offer an alternative reading. I feel I am currently in danger of loosening my grip on *my* Rimbaud, and I am ill-prepared for such an eventuality. Perhaps, in some way, I would go so far as to say that I actually resent the intrusion.

Then, before I can formulate these ideas into some sort of riposte, a very curious thing occurs.

Madame Autry leans over and, with little or no ceremony, she takes my hand in hers. 'Don't worry,' she says after a few moments' silence.

And I realise in the same instant that I have been holding my breath.

9. INVENTIONS

'L'amour est à réinventer.'

Love has to be reinvented.

This line, which features in the 'Déliries 1' section of *Une Saison en Enfer*, is one of Rimbaud's most frequently quoted. It is not difficult to understand why. It is a bold statement and has the additional virtue of already sounding like a slogan. Or a call to arms. Indeed, during the student uprising of May 1968, graffiti featuring quotes from Rimbaud were frequently seen on the walls of Paris buildings. At this distance, I have no way of knowing if that particular line was actually used, but I always thought it would have been my first choice.

But subsequently and perhaps a little begrudgingly, I have begun to read the term a little differently. Rimbaud is not declaring that our experience of love needs to be expanded upon, but rather that it needs to be *reinvented*. Not redefined or recreated. Reinvented. To me, Rimbaud is clearly suggesting that love was invented or man-made in the first instance. A human construct – something cynical and mechanical. An ancient historical device to encourage pair-bonding and to subvert mankind's more pagan, baser instincts.

This is a depressing theory, but during darker times in my life, when – like so many others – I have sought the marvellous consolations of fatalism; I have taken some final, desperate comfort from it. But I concede the words are of very little consequence to me nowadays, beyond the fact that they just unexpectedly jumped into my head the moment I parted company from Madame Autry.

Our actual parting was brief and hardly worth commenting upon. We had walked back to La Place Ducale together, at which point she thanked me for the beer, kissed me on the cheek and wandered off in the direction of the town hall. She explained that she was currently sleeping on a fold-out bed at her friend's house, a favour for which she was expected to keep the house tidy and run a few errands. It was one of these particular duties, I presume, that was responsible for bringing our conversation by the river to a halt.

I catch myself watching her as she walks away, and I wonder if I will see her again. She has just told me that we could continue our conversation tomorrow, but this, I fear, suggested a simple pleasantry rather than an actual firm arrangement. I push my hands back into my pockets and feel the receipt for the beer I bought for us earlier. I close my eyes and smile, and then I make a bold attempt at that studied casual nonchalance for which I will never be famous.

I avoid the main shopping precinct and, instead, make my way down Rue du Petit-Bois. To my left, just about visible over the rooftops are the rather impressive twin spires of Eglise Saint Rémi. It was in their shadow that Rimbaud once famously (or apocryphally) scrawled on the pavement: '*Merde* à *Dieu*'.

Perhaps shitting on God was an act of atheistic rebellion or spiritual defiance, but to me, it shares some similarities with his attitude towards love. It wasn't a question of doubting its existence, but more a growing suspicion that it was no longer necessary or had any sort of place in his world.

I suppose we trust ourselves that we love and that we are loved, but in truth, we have no real way of knowing. We just blunder through life convinced that this latest shameful, pointless encounter means more than the previous one, or that this connection is stronger, better and infinitely more worthwhile than those in the past. But do we think this simply because we want to think this? Because it suits our current needs and our situations? These needs ultimately manifest themselves in a sort of *emotional materialism* for which we are always far too quick to forgive ourselves. In that respect, should the concept of love be re-evaluated if not totally reinvented?

It's not about finding love any more; it's about finding a situation that distracts you from mourning its absence.

Absence...

Then I hear her voice over the traffic.

'No, no, *monsieur*! You must stop trying to use cynicism as a general anaesthetic! It doesn't work! In fact, it has never worked. You just thought it did! And just how long exactly do you intend to confuse pessimism with envy? It is your silly vanity. People like you love the idea that they are too clever and too educated to ever be fooled by a concept as vague and nefarious as love! Besides, your Rimbaud had no faith in God or love, yet he somehow managed to believe that he could change the whole course of human history through his poetry! No, I don't think so. This is nothing more than traditional, normal adolescent nihilism...'

With some effort, I repress my smile and turn around.

But there is nobody there.

Just the still, cruel, indifferent afternoon breathing a warm sigh into my stupid face.

And out of the blue, without warning, I'm thinking about absence again.

I continue walking towards the junction with Rue Forest, and now, as I think about returning to my hotel, I remind myself of that wonderful line in 'Enfance' in *Les Illuminations*:

'*On suit la route rouge pour arrive à l'auberge vide.*'

You follow the red road to arrive at the empty inn.

One hesitates to think one's life can be so glibly yet accurately summarised, yet I find myself returning to this quote with depressing regularity nowadays. Indeed, I feel I have been walking that precise, solitary route for as long as I can remember. A life is so clearly signposted; it is literally a red road, and thus has a sense of direction and intention. We devote our whole lives to this quest, but its purpose is utterly illusory. There was never any real, tangible objective; it is missing, abandoned and *absent*, and we have only ever been pursuing the ghosts of actual meaning.

But in truth, it is neither the journey nor its destination nor even the absurd notion that they are in some way connected. Rimbaud understood this; he knew the difference between what is unknowable and what is simply unknown. For years, he dedicated himself to the pursuit of this exact idea, whilst the rest of us still have no alternative other than to keep following the red road.

'*Merde!*'

'Pah! "*L'égoisme infini d'adolesence.*'" The words are spoken by a weary yet familiar female voice. 'That is actually *his* precise expression and not mine, monsieur! The infinite egotism of adolescence!'

'… *la voix féminine arrivée au fond des volcans et des grottes arctiques.*'[16]

'Oh be quiet! You forget you are from Charleville, boy! What do you know of volcanoes and arctic grottoes, huh?'

'*Ma camarade, mendiante, enfant monster…*'[17]

'Oh please… and what then are you exactly?'

---

16   … and the female voice that reaches the depths of volcanoes and artic grottoes.

17   My companion, beggar-girl, child monster…

'*Je suis maitre du silence.*'[18]

'No, you are the master of very little, and your silence – for most of us, to be honest – is a positive blessing…'

'*Merde!*'

At this precise moment, I lose my balance very slightly as I turn my ankle and topple off the pavement into the road. Thankfully, I am unobserved, but I am forced, rather ashamedly, to admit I really am not much of a beer drinker nowadays. With slightly less dexterity than I would have wished, I straighten my back and regain my posture. For a moment, confused and accusing, I stare down at the kerb, as I hear another voice.

It is a different female voice.

The first voice I ever heard.

A voice as old as I am.

'Careful, darling! For goodness' sake! I know how much Rimbaud means to you, but I really don't think he's worth getting yourself killed for!'

I feel my nostrils flare as I exhale slowly. 'OK, Mum.'

'Life is precious, you know, and it's all we have.'

'OK, OK…'

'Just don't waste *all* your days thinking! This is the only life you are ever going to get! There is nothing else! Your annihilation awaits you, so try not to go actively seeking it!'

She wasn't a particularly vociferous or belligerent atheist, by any means, yet in these past few months, I seem to have imbued her with a number of not-dissimilar general viewpoints.

'I'll do my best…' I say as glibly as I am able.

'Do you know that I can't actually remember the last time I saw you happy or even smiling.' She sighs theatrically, a technique with which I am all too familiar. 'You must really try to take advantage of… well, you know…'

'I don't think I do, and that's probably the problem.'

---

18 I am the master of silence.

'Oh, just look around you, darling. It's such a beautiful, glorious afternoon. I never thought I'd say this, but there really is so much more to life than books. Sadly, you do know that you will die one day and I can't prevent it from happening, so please try your best to live a little before then.'

I think I slightly resent the vague underlying implication in her suggestion, but I manage to sound wounded rather than reproachful: 'Thanks, I'll bear that in mind.'

But feeling slightly more exposed than I might have wished, I begin to walk a little faster as I attempt to divert the current course of our conversation. 'Do you remember, Mum?' I ask in hurried, slightly nervous tones. 'About three years ago, we had a conversation about death? I admit it sounds silly now, but I think I was actually trying to cheer you up! Does it ring any bells? I told you that I imagined it being like this. Like there is an unexpected rushing sound, like the approach of an underground train, all traces and echoes but lacking any original source. Louder and louder, intense and unbearable, the audial equivalent of a blinding light. In the sound, you can actually glimpse faces and recall rooms, intimacies and betrayals. The sound builds to an inevitable climax, a moment of complete revelation and awareness. You flinch and cower, and you wait for the final moment, the great denouement, but then there is nothing. A sudden terrifying absence of everything: of all consciousness and being. Just the breathless un-living stillness of non-existence. The only presence is the recognition of absence. A blank, unending void. You are at the very moment of extinction. The terrible emptiness surrounds you and absorbs you. You wait, but on some level, that implies time – and time no longer exists. Everything is nothing: a deep, endless, impenetrable silent darkness; an eternal black permanence. There is nothing now – only the fading memory of awareness. But then, abruptly, there is a row of shapes in the blackness; you count them, and there are seventeen in what appears to be four distinct, irregular groups. So you adjust your eyes, and as you do so, the figures seem to modify – they change their physical form and colour, and they begin to move towards you out of the infinite night. You see they are in a constant state of transformation, like some accelerated lifecycle, until they activate something deep within your memory. When the process is finally complete, you see in clear, white text, etched into the very fabric of the void itself, the following words: "Based on a true story".

'Yes, darling, of course I remember that. Oh, I tell everyone that you could always make me laugh.'

'Yeah, Mum, I guess I was still capable of being frivolous back then.'

She exhales slowly and dramatically, her usual method of indicating her impatience with me. 'Oh darling, you shouldn't have such a low opinion of yourself, you know?' she adds, in what I am pleased to note are more conventionally sympathetic tones.

'I think I have a natural gift for it,' I say after a moment's reflection. 'Vain, self-absorbed, hypochondriac mummy's boy, without the obvious vindication of actually having a mummy nowadays.'

'Oh darling...'

'*Merde!*'

'Oh Christ! Not now!'

'*Et la Mère... satisfaite et très fière sans voir...*'[19]

'Oh, fuck off and leave them in peace why don't you?' asks a different female voice, in what have now become familiar tones of exasperation.

'*Comme un mendiante sur les quais de marbre...*'[20]

'Is that it?' she queries, her voice loaded with its customary disgust. 'Is that really the most pertinent thing you can find to say to me?'

---

19 And the Mother... satisfied and very proud, without seeing...
20 Like a beggar on the marble quaysides

She lets out a wordless exclamation that implies both tedium and disgust, before saying 'I think, Monsieur Marc, it would be best if you went back to your hotel now and maybe had a bit of a rest. You do look a little tired...'

'You don't know the half of it...' I respond, my voice booming far louder than the circumstances warrant. At the same moment, I lose my balance again slightly.

'Be careful, *monsieur*.'

'I'm fine,' I hiss, and I attempt a casual dismissive shrug, which proves to be a ridiculously ill-timed idea, as once again, I slip off the kerb.

She stifles a laugh. '*Monsieur*?'

I smile bravely, but say nothing.

She seems to take this as a cue to change the subject. 'Your mother, I think, is very nice, yes?'

'Far too much faith in humanity and far too little faith in humans.' I mutter under my breath.

'Your mother?'

'No, that is what she always used to say about me. She was often, maybe too often, how would you say...? Refreshingly candid?'

'And was she right, do you think? Is it true?'

I inhale.

Then I forget to exhale.

Then, finally, I exhale.

'I don't know. I think it was just a flippant remark she made once. But it was one of those brilliantly glib comments parents make from time to time that are rendered immortal in the minds of their children. They haunt them for the entire duration of their days, never losing a fraction of their original power or capacity to hurt.'

Now she is unable to supress her laugh. 'So, she was right, then?'

'No idea,' I say as honestly as I am able. 'On balance... er, probably not.'

'Oh Marc, you know what they say? A little knowledge is a dangerous thing, whereas a little self-knowledge – in my experience – is usually fucking catastrophic!'

All of a sudden, I am feeling angry – something not dissimilar to jealously perhaps. 'How come you get all the best lines?'

'*Monsieur*?'

'I'm serious. The cemetery, the bar, the river...' My voice trails off as the anger quickly mutates into a quiet, almost meditative melancholy. 'All the good lines are coming from you. It's like I'm just here setting them up for you...'

'I'm sure,' she begins, with a new evident confidence, 'it will all balance out eventually, and the situation will change.'

I remind her that this is my book and those decisions should be mine and mine alone. 'Ultimately,' I conclude, 'you are supposed to represent my '*autre*'. I mean, come on, that's obvious. You are just indicative of a particular thought process. Actually, my original intention was to make you something akin to the voice of traditional unorthodoxy. That's all. That is your entire purpose and function!' I shake my head apologetically. 'When all is said and done, you are just a method of putting across original, perhaps spontaneous thinking that runs counter to my own slightly more conventional take on things.'

But I realise I am talking to myself.

I am alone with just the lowering sun on the warm, glowing afternoon street.

10. Abyss (i)

I awake from my sleep, grateful that I had the foresight to remove my shoes.

Or remove one of them at least.

The bed feels hot and crumpled underneath me as I swing my legs around and attempt to sit up. Some hitherto largely ignored function of my inner ear chooses this precise moment to fail quite spectacularly, and I sense the room spinning wildly around me.

With some difficulty, by steadying myself on the small bedside unit and knocking my phone off it in the process, I eventually manage to stand up. I have never felt comfortable with the consequences of inebriation, be it mine or anyone else's, and as I stagger rather pathetically to the bathroom, the only tiny grain of relief lies in the fact that I am blessedly unobserved in my current state.

I disappoint myself by how little I feel like vomiting – usually my Hogarthian epicentre of self-loathing and moral failure at times like this one – and instead, I run some cold water into my cupped hands. I then raise my hands to my mouth and take a few sips, but the water tastes of rust and warm dirt, so I spit it out.

As I do so, I catch sight of my reflection briefly. After a moment or two, I recognise myself. I am the mad, weather-beaten, sun-fucked, demonic uncle of the person who was here earlier. I want to shake my head, but I suspect such an activity might be fractionally beyond my capacity at the moment. So instead, I let out slowly a somnambulistic, wordless noise – the sense of which, I imagine, is probably fairly universal.

I steal a second glance in the mirror as I find my voice again: 'Sometimes, you stare at the abyss, and the abyss just doesn't think you're worth staring back at...'

This, I tell myself is actually not a bad line for a change, and it might be a good idea if I made a note of it.

Or alternatively: 'Sometimes, you stare at the abyss, but the abyss thinks you're a bit of a twat and pretends to ignore you.'

Better?

Not sure.

Maybe not 'twat'...

'Wanker?'

Now, with something approaching a renewed sense of purpose, I make my way slowly and gracelessly back towards the bedroom. With some effort, I push open the single heavy, dark curtain that I have no memory of having closed earlier. It is still light. It is the unmistakeable light of an early evening in midsummer that forever glimmers with unspoken promise and possibility. Our lives cast wide open and revealed, and suddenly illuminated with love and mystery – a bell of pink fire rings in the clouds! And I thus calculate, more mundanely, that I might have been dozing for an hour or so, but certainly no longer.

In time – with the ancient, natural rhythm of the moment – my eyes close and open as they adjust to the light, and there he is again. By his neat, little path and the neat, low, little fountain, on his lovely plinth with the lyre motif. He fixes his polished-marble stare on me again.

'*Mais pour après, se coucher dans la merde...*'[21]

I frown back at him. 'No, no; it's not that bad, really. It was only a couple of beers.'

'*Petite veille d'ivresse, sainte!*'[22]

'Oh, come on. I thought you were all in favour of the disorientation of the senses?'

There is a pause during which I distinctly sense a conversational advantage.

'*L'art est une sottise...*'[23]

'That's an obscure one! But no, you don't get away with it so easily. And that's another thing, isn't it? This whole derangement or disorientation of the senses, as you call it – it's absolutely central to your whole way of thinking, isn't it?' I ask rhetorically. 'Actually, it's beyond even that! It's the ultimate alchemy by which you seek to transform yourself into a *voyant* or a seer, am I right?' Rhetorical again.

Now I wait in vain for the usual single-syllable interjection.

So I continue in a voice that is suddenly no longer mine but is that of a French woman in a striped T-shirt. 'So when do you think your whole concept became hijacked as the artistic justification we trot out too regularly to forgive our great cultural and artistic heroes for episodes of general hedonism and overindulgence, huh? The famous Rimbaudian quest for self-actualisation. You know the story – every time some fucked-up, second-rate rock star falls into the gutter, somebody somewhere invokes your name! It's pathetic; really, it is! It's nothing beyond the lowest journalistic cliché – and you should know. You really do have a lot to answer for! Truthfully, it's a shameful terrible legacy that all your silly followers have inflicted on you. I'm serious,

21 But afterwards, to sleep in shit...
22 Small drunken vigil, holy!
23 Art is a foolishness...

boy! For so long, so much stupidity has been taking place in your honour! This is usually by people who completely fail to understand you – those who instead concentrate only on the tawdry mythology that surrounds you. People who find some great eternal purpose to their lives by rummaging hopelessly through yours.'

'*Merde!*'

'Oh, and there it is,' I say in an unremarkable, quiet English voice, yet one that is reassuringly my own once again.

I turn away from the window, a fairly obvious device that suggests movement away from the external towards the internal, or in my case, away from the '*autre*' to the '*je*'. I reach into my rucksack and take out my tablet, and for a moment, I enjoy this sense of renewed purpose and intention. This is a book I can write, I tell myself, a book I should write and a book I want to write. Perhaps in my own head, I have been writing it for years. I had to be old enough to feel I no longer had to prove anything to myself. Or that I could confess and not feel the burden of shame or the need for atonement.

But as I quickly discover, the tablet needs charging and posterity must wait a little longer.

So now, battling to be heard above the voices of his characters, is this the point when the author reveals something of himself to his reader? Should he take this opportunity to expand on his ideas? Elaborate a little more on his back story?

Maybe.

It is certainly true that, when I'd first woken up a few minutes ago, I had experienced a moment of rare clarity with a very particular, specific idea right at the very front of my mind. Somewhere in the great mountain of shit I have read in my life (but I have forgotten the specific source) is this clear notion that, rather than being male, Adam was actually a hermaphrodite. He was made male only after the creation of Eve – effectively his female alter ego, as he is hers.

There is a welcome breeze through the window that agitates the curtains slightly, and I am aware of the subtlest modification to the shadows being cast on the opposite wall.

'It is not that obscure, *monsieur*.'

Instinctively, I shut my eyes, my mouth hovering at the outskirts of a smile. 'Oh no, really?'

'Well, it's actually in the Bible, Marc, so I'd hardly be regarding that as arcane, would you?'

'Well, I don't know; I'm—'

'Also, it is kind of right there on fucking page one too! Genesis chapter 1 verse 27. Adam is made with both male and female characteristics. The image of his creator, in fact.'

'Oh Anne, how do you even know that?'

'Eh? Your question? I do not think I am understanding...'

I open my eyes again, but I don't turn around – although I sense I am alone once more. 'Seriously now, how can you actually know about that if I, as the writer, don't have access to that information myself?'

I welcome the silence that follows my question, I sit on the corner of the bed and, for a moment, I put my head in my hands. Then, unexpectedly, in this perfect mute evening, as my thoughts begin to clear, my mind returns to Adam, and I feel something connect. It's a memory that reaches out of the darkness to become an idea, and like Rimbaud, I feel I am present at the birth of my own thinking. Then I lose it again. It falls away from me; it drifts through my hands like, like...

But I can only hear my own breathing now and feel the memory of the warmth of the day on my skin.

I glance down at my feet, still with only the one shoe between them, and I suddenly wonder if I'm looking at the simplest metaphor of all. Left, right, same, different, *je*, *autre* – and there it is again, that germ of an idea...

Plato believed that consciousness pre-exists birth, that we are born with knowledge and awareness, and that education is not about learning but more about remembering. In that respect, his thinking was not too dissimilar to some contemporary theories about the multiverse. Aristotle, who was Plato's most renowned pupil, shared his teacher's belief in a conscious life preceding the corporeal one. Crucially, he also adhered to the fundamentals of Plato's idea, as set out in *The Symposium*, that we exist in an incomplete, divided state and are constantly questing after our own perfect mirror image.

However, his philosophy did differ in one notable respect: Aristotle advocated that individual consciousness – or what might be theologically termed the 'soul', if you prefer – was simultaneously both male and female and had, in effect, no specific gender. These characteristics were only made manifest at the moment of physical birth. At which point, we are divided into masculine and feminine components that thereafter inhabit a man's or a woman's body. Two distinct and separate, presumably compatible, halves of a once-perfect unity are created, just as the original hermaphroditic state is rendered forever incomplete.

(Actually, when you think about it – and I've always found this quite interesting – considering that it's such an obscure, largely forgotten theory, it is strange to think that one can still find linguistic echoes in the ongoing vernacular of *romantic cliché*. People will refer to their soul mate, their other half, etc. This could be seen as a very simplified take on precisely the point Aristotle was making.)

Then, a couple of months ago, I read online a paper published by an American university that set forth the theory that the human race did actually evolve from hermaphroditic ancestors. Basically, this was Aristotle's ideas being re-evaluated in a broadly scientific context. Admittedly, the research is still very much in its infancy, but it throws up any number of fascinating questions.

I really don't know enough about the subject to even

speculate, but it is surely of some interest that, in the works of an ancient Greek philosopher and again in the Bible, we come across this very similar concept of a hermaphroditic ancestry prior to the species' separation into genders?

Anyway, the reason why all this is on my mind at present is largely, I imagine, as an alternative to the critical rigidity of Rimbaud's *autre*. His idea of the *autre* was of something distinct yet strongly connected to and even controlled by the self. But Aristotle's premise that we are incomplete and divided and thus apart from our more literal *autre* seems of particular interest, given some of the themes of my book.

I stand up again, noticing with a sense of relief that the dizziness seems to be subsiding now, and I retrieve from my rucksack the couple of pages of handwritten notes I'd made on the train earlier. I scan them quickly for anything that might be relevant to what is currently focussing my mind, but I find nothing worthwhile. I read the lines:

The destination doesn't matter.
The point of departure is of little consequence.
Even the journey itself will give me not a moment's pause.
My spirit will be contained only in the music I listen to along the way.

These are followed by a few comments about the nature of bereavement and a paragraph or two on Rimbaud's quest for suitable adult-male role models – a pursuit that seemed to last until, significantly, he became an adult male himself. But there is little else of interest.

I let the notes fall to the floor, I lie back down on the bed and I close my eyes again.

A few minutes pass, then a few more, and there she is again. It seems as though she has been there all my life, but I now know who she is. I have never spoken of her before to anyone. Although, perhaps paradoxically, I have made references to her in a couple of my earlier novels, where I once possibly imagined I could hide behind some authorial privilege of anonymity. Or that the idea is simply a momentary whimsy in an otherwise tedious narrative.

But she is there.

She has always been there.

A presence without form or substance, and a constant peripheral companion – never seen, but known, felt, understood, and just glimpsed in dreams or at that moment between waking and sleeping. There has also been this curious vague awareness of some silhouetted figure periodically occupying the very limits of my field of vision. A benign, beautiful image of a woman, whose soft, gentle hand I will always seek at times of crisis or emotional pain.

Sorry, Rimbaud, but according to my admittedly rapidly shifting definitions, she is and always has been my *autre*.

She has actually been with me longer than you have!

I first wrote about her over twenty years ago:

I know her name,
I have always known her name.
I knew her name before I knew my own,
Before I was even born
Before there was even language.
She has always been there.
She had taken many forms,
I had chased the sound of her voice
In waves crashing against distant shores,
I had gazed at the rising sun and glimpsed her smile.
I had followed the echo of her footsteps down dark corridors
And heard her name repeated endlessly
As the sound of my own racing heartbeat.

Then, about ten years later, I returned to a similar theme:

When I loved her.
I loved all things.
I loved a language that gave me her name.
I worshipped a sun that gave me the light that I might see her.
I loved my own hands, for they had felt her beauty.
I loved the wall where once she had cast a shadow.
I loved the shape in the pillow where once she had laid her head.
There, I traced the letters of her name across the hearts of all men.

A now all-too-familiar voice booms from Place de la Gare, coming in through the open window:

'*L'histoire d'une de mes folies…*'[24]

'Oh, do shut up! God, he can be annoying! Don't listen to him, Marc. It is only the continuing resentment and bitterness of failure! Don't let him put you off. Anyway, perhaps you are making an homage, I think, to *Une Saison en Enfer*, here? Those passages in 'Alchimie du Verbe', where he quotes examples of his earlier work.'

I rigorously scratch the hair above my ear. 'I really don't think it was intentional.'

'But I thought it was like having single-word titles as chapter headings. Is that not you intentionally making textual allusions to the titles of *Les Illuminations*?'

Possibly out of embarrassment or simply vanity, I decide to ignore her question. 'But maybe he's right. Maybe this is simply not the time.'

'No, *monsieur*, you shouldn't think about him. It is good that you are considering alternatives. And I thought what you were saying about Aristotle was quite interesting. That, secretly, we are all searching for and questing after our mythical other half and alter ego. I presume if, as Plato supposes, education is remembering, then it follows that love's highest purpose would

---

24   The story of one of my follies

ultimately be a reunion. Or perhaps "reunification" would be an even better word. This would make the act more like conjoining rather than simply making love, would it not? As I recall, there are actual direct references to this in *The Symposium*. I don't know, maybe buried deep in our DNA is this ancient need to actually find our perfect, well, *autre*.' She enunciates the word carefully and without irony.

'I don't know,' I offer apologetically.

'But how would you recognise or even know that you had found your *autre*? What is it? Maybe when they fuck, their bits would fit together perfectly, yes?' She laughs half-heartedly.

I'm not sure whether she is being serious, but I do sense that she might be teasing me.

'I guess,' I say, exhaling loudly, with my tone now deliberately calm and expressionless, 'all couples in some way create their own mythologies – they exaggerate the significance of coincidence and random events in order to emphasise some shared, laughable delusion of predeterminism.'

Her voice is now suddenly stern and rebuking. 'And there you go with the cynicism again, *monsieur*! I cannot sympathise with your views, but neither would I wish to!'

Love is actually completely irrelevant to the survival of the species; it always has been, just nobody thought to check! This probably makes me sound bitter and misanthropic and generally awful, so I would hesitate to say it out loud or record it in any way. But love is no more vital to our continued existence than, say, music or painting. It is in that respect not an instinct, as such, and therefore you could argue that it is not a natural impulse. It scares and unsettles us, obviously, and we are inevitably frightened by it – hence we seek methods of making it tangible, certain, secure. We have the conventions of marriage, the family unit and children, yet that fear always remains. Whilst we might like to believe we are in active pursuit of love, we are often simply chasing after the emblems of its certainty.

And, therefore, proof of its existence.

Love is the driving force in our lives, yet it is entirely unnatural.

'Yes, and very possibly ridiculous,' suggests Anne Autry.

'And thank fuck for that,' we say together.

11. Abyss (ii)

After dozing for a further twenty minutes, I open my eyes again to discover that my head feels surprisingly clear and I am recalling, with a quite perplexing level of clarity, passages in an article I wrote about fifteen years ago. It was actually a review for a book about W.B. Yeats. Whilst I would never claim to have the intellectual audacity to write in a scholarly manner about a writer of his magnitude, the book in question was not a standard biography. It was mainly an account of Yeats' lifelong fascination with the occult and the paranormal. I wrote, I think, about 1,300 words, got paid and forgot about it.

Or forgot *mostly* about it as a few aspects of the book have evidently remained with me.

Particularly, now in this hotel room in Charleville, so many years and so many lives away.

As the evening accelerates towards the conclusions and consolations of dusk, I find that Yeats and the book in particular have a sudden relevance to me and my current frame of mind. (He was, I recall, born only eleven years after Rimbaud, but again, he appears to be from some completely different era.)

As I clearly remember, my review made several references to the central dichotomy in any approach or summation of Yeats. Specifically, the inherent contradiction between the literary genius – arguably the greatest English language poet of the twentieth century – and the man who believed in fairies, mediums and leprechauns.

But maybe I was missing something then; maybe I still am. Maybe that is the point. Maybe the hallmark of genius lies in the recognition that no such distinction can reasonably be drawn. One result of which being the enviable capacity to embrace the irrational and all the inherent possibilities contained therein.

Perhaps it is the ability to discriminate between the irrational and the evidently impossible. It is a distinction that is far harder to make than one might imagine. Maybe it wasn't that Yeats regarded leprechauns as real, in any sense of the word, but simply that he didn't feel he had the absolute authority to judge their existence to be impossible. Could I perhaps tie in Yeats' accommodation of the irrational with Rimbaud's quest for the unknown? I might be able to at some point, but my thoughts have drifted elsewhere once again…

I admit that it is deeply irrational to even speculate that we might be descendants of hermaphrodites. But would Yeats have considered it impossible? Doubtful. (It is more than a little significant, perhaps, that he referenced Plato's ideas about perfect other halves, likening them to egg yolks and egg whites in a single shell, in the second verse of one of his most famous poems, 'Among School Children.')

But purely as an intellectual exercise alone, if we extrapolate this idea further, would it also be impossible that, somewhere out there in the world, somewhere amongst the countless millions of souls, there might exist a descendant of the same intersex ancestor – someone who might therefore share some tiny trace of inherited DNA? A person who, on some ancient, microscopic level might therefore correspond to this actual romantic idea of a human individual's fabled other half.

The 'Aristotelian *autre*'.

(It's only been about an hour, but I have to say that I am already rather taken with this expression.)

Now, even without accepting such a hypothesis, it should be regarded as beyond unlikely that the lives of these two individuals would ever intersect. Therefore, it can be concluded, without a moment's pause, that the whole idea is absurd. Irrational even. But Yeats, I still feel, would hesitate to use the word 'impossible'. Perhaps he would even be correct in this, as what cannot be deemed categorically and empirically impossible must therefore be judged, however unlikely, to remain in the realm of the possible.

Sadly, I note that, for me, like Yeats himself, the temptations of the irrational have become more seductive during middle age.

'Oh, surely,' says a voice that is still locked between awakenings and justly honoured for its decades of patience and tolerance, 'you're not thinking, are you, about that… *lady?*' Intentionally or otherwise, she gives the word a peculiar emphasis.

'Do you mind, Mum?' I ask, my voice bypassing wounded altogether in favour of pure adolescent truculence. 'You can't just barge in here like this. I am entitled to some privacy, you know? You could knock or something.' I stand up, and in doing so, I notice that I am still only wearing one shoe.

'You see, there you go again. You seem forever burdened with this hilarious illusion that you can actually keep a secret from your own mother.'

'What?' I maintain, without difficulty, my previous level of spotty hostility.

'You are definitely thinking about that lady. I just knew it.'

'What lady?' I mumble quickly, hoping to mask any suggestion of embarrassment.

'Oh darling, you know very well whom I'm talking about. The scruffy lady you met outside the supermarket. You know the… the…'

'*Mendiante…*'[25] says the voice from the Place de la Gare.

'Thank you, dear.'

I hear myself sigh, after which the room falls into silence for a few moments.

'Anyway,' I say eventually, uncertain to whom I am actually addressing my comments. 'I wasn't thinking about anyone in particular. I just felt that, as an alternative to Rimbaud's *autre*, it was an idea worth exploring.'

'Oh please; really? A beggar for pity's sake? The imagery alone suggests something ghastly and Pre-Raphaelite. Or biblical even. Do try to show some self-respect, darling.'

'*Merde!*'

'It's the truth. Sorry…' I say, not feeling sorry in the slightest.

'Oh, you were always so much braver when you were younger; you had so much more confidence and conviction in your own ideas too.'

'It's just idle speculation, Mum. Just something to think about. Look, the odds against actually being born in the first place are so incalculably, cosmically high. The odds against finding your true *autre*, your second self, are surely no higher.'

The chuckle teeters on the self-satisfied. 'You know, in the old days, you always used to be a lot better at squirming away from awkward questions and changing the subject too.'

I shake my head. 'No, Mum, it's just… really, it's nothing. Honestly. It was mainly considering what might have been Yeats' perspective on all—'

'I do understand; of course I do. I am your mother. And it would make such a great story if she were your… your other self or whatever you call it. But I think you're just wasting your time

---

25 Beggar girl…

when you really need to be focussing now on your actual book idea.'

'But like I explained, this does link in to one of the main themes of the—'

'And really, darling, it's not a very likely scenario, is it? I know you must feel rather alone in the world right now, abandoned even, and perhaps you just want to feel a strong connection to someone – anyone, for that matter – and I understand that; of course I do… But do forget all about Yeats and Aristotle.' She intones their names darkly as though they might have been some questionable vaudeville act or the brand of a once popular cough remedy. 'Why don't you try to concentrate on Rimbaud again now?'

I am grateful that she has managed not to comment any further on Anne's lowly circumstances, which, sadly, wouldn't have surprised me. I do, however, feel she is missing the point of my argument quite spectacularly. 'Are you actually listening to me at all?'

'Look, as the two of you were walking back together to La Place Ducale earlier, it was so obvious. She was walking fractionally behind you, but then you caught sight of her out of the corner of your eye, didn't you? In silhouette? The recognition was instant and unequivocal. A figure without form or substance. Just that one single essential, permanent truth. The greatest destiny of all: profound, inevitable, but nothing beyond that initial glimpse – just the implication of perfection as a recalled memory. She reminded you of that shadowy, peripheral figure you spoke of, didn't she? Didn't she?'

But the voice is no longer that of my late mother. The voice is once again my own. I close my eyes and recite from memory, mechanically:

Neither shatter nor demean,
Those little hoops through which we dream.

You see, Mum, we all need one of those little hoops now and again. It just seems as though I might need mine more than most right now. They are sometimes, perhaps all the time, the only thing that makes life endurable. As I stumble, moment by atomic moment, towards non-existence. Does it really matter to me or to you or to anyone that my purpose remains unrevealed? Who will tell my story? Where's my Sir Thomas? Why do all ruminations of this nature ultimately manifest themselves to me as anxieties? Did I inherit this trait from you? Did you have days like this? Was I so self-absorbed I never noticed? I sought instead comfort and answers in punk rock and Rimbaud, but I never once thought to glance over my own shoulder.

Gosh, everyone! How clever and enlightened we all were...

I shake myself free of this particular reverie as I see Anne's face clearly in my mind once again. Except, in truth, I don't see it clearly at all. I see her various individual features with stunning lucidity: the impudent curve of her top lip, the sublime arc of her eyebrows and those dark scrying-mirrors of her eyes. Yet if I attempt to draw all the elements together into a composite image in my mind, the exercise ends in chaos and disarray. There is some vital and tangible aspect that still eludes me. If I'm honest, it is something that makes her seem infinitely more attractive.

'*Un soir, j'ai assis la Beauté sur mes genoux.*'[26]

Oh, hello again...

'*Et je l'ai trouvée amère – et je l'ai injuriée.*'[27]

Thank you, but you know, I never really understood how anyone was quite that bitter and cynical at twenty. Was it all actually an act, some kind of prolonged adolescent tantrum functioning as a defence mechanism? Does it all go back to your issues with your mother? And no, I don't really want to get into that at the moment.

---

26 One night, I sat beauty on my knee.

27 I found her bitter – and I insulted her.

'Toutes les forms d'amour, de souffrance, de folie...'[28]

Not now; I'm really not in the mood. Although, to be honest, I don't know what mood I am in any more. I seem to be currently oscillating between mild infatuation and bereavement, and noting the curious similarities as I do so. Common to both is the inability to find a single term or an expression that accurately summarises and defines my' own feelings. There is also this increasing sense that all our realities, and all our certainties, amount to little more than the random static from an old, abandoned TV set left on in a forgotten room somewhere – there is a degree of awareness, even a curiosity, but there is very little beyond that.

Absent.

Elsewhere.

Evident, furthermore, is this growing conviction that time can no longer be measured accurately by conventional means. Hours, months, years, recent, ancient, too soon, far too soon – all are terms that have been redefined personally and intuitively.

Craving distraction now, I wander over to the window again and stare out over the square. It is getting dark, and he is less visible now; from this angle, he is slightly obscured behind the branches of the trees that line the surrounding path. But no, not hidden, just camouflaged. And he is silent now. He can wait; he has the merciless patience of a trained killer – a true assassin.

Then, without really thinking what I am doing, following an impulse I can barely articulate and without turning around, I reach my hand out behind me.

No more than a moment later, I feel a hand grasping mine.

Our fingers entwine.

I smile as I whisper,

'Neither shatter nor demean,
Those little hoops through which we dream.'

---

28   All forms of love, of suffering, of madness

12. Youth

Artichokes.

Thousands of them.

As far as the horizon and, one imagines, probably far beyond that too.

Artichokes in number beyond your wildest imaginings.

A mathematically incalculable number of artichokes.

In fact, the landscape in the morning sun used to always trick the eye into reading repetition and repeating patterns; this was agriculture conforming to the William Morris fabric principle. It was a view I photographed more than once on my old Instamatic camera, yet my memory seems quite capable of recalling the scene without assistance.

And so it comes to mind again as I wake up the following morning after my first night in Hôtel Couleurs Sud. After pulling open the curtains, gazing out over the square and then perhaps deliberately upwards at the shimmering, cloudless azure of the early morning, I convince myself that the skies over all French provincial towns exude this very specific blueness and stillness at this hour in the summer. And thus I am transported back to

Brittany in the mid-1970s; I'm about fourteen, and my lasting impression of my first ever trip abroad mainly features fucking artichokes.

My previously mentioned comprehensive school was in a town twinned with a similarly sized town in Brittany, and every year, third- and fourth-form French students were invited to join the student exchange programme. A French student stayed with my family for a fortnight, and the following year, I went to stay with him and his family in Brittany. What I was so spectacularly ill-prepared for was the fact that he and his family lived a long, long way away from town on a farm. An artichoke farm to be specific, and for two weeks – aside from rare visits to relatives of the family – I spent the entire time amongst artichokes and people whose lives seemed to be pretty much governed by artichokes.

Prior to this particular fortnight, I'd had very little exposure to artichokes – certainly not enough to form a strong opinion on the subject. Subsequently, however, I admit my view became a little embittered, and to this day, whilst I might regard them as a perfectly acceptable heraldic emblem – comparable to a crow or a raven – their suitability as a main course should similarly be approached with a degree of caution.

It was not easy.

I was homesick and bored, and I cried a lot.

Usually when I went to bed.

But the most curious thing occurred about the third night of my stay. Based on some impulse I have never been able to fathom, I decided that I should, at some point, write a book about my experiences. Seriously. I envisaged the work as a sort of semi-autobiographical comedic novel, detailing my adventures and portraying the immediate family and their colourful relatives in a humorous and pithy way. I had the whole thing worked out and started reciting chunks out loud to myself. It would naturally be a huge success, I told myself, and doubtless be adapted into a movie at some point.

The strangest aspect in all this was that, at that age, I had not the slightest interest in books or reading, and I don't actually think I'd ever read a novel. I was interested in music and football, and the very few books I actually owned reflected this. So, to this day, I have not the remotest idea where the sudden urge came from, although it was one that, naturally, was forgotten the day I returned home. It seemed, I suppose, something from which I might gain some comfort and that would lend reason or purpose to my experiences. It was a new role, a new character and one that would enrich my life with a very satisfying objectivity – the precise objectivity through which I could avoid getting myself sullied by any direct contact with pain or sadness.

It was, however, the first time I had ever considered that writing of any kind could play even the most obscure role in my life. Rimbaud sought to reinvent literature; I merely wanted to get through the fortnight without snivelling too loudly at mealtimes. I honestly think it was right there and at that precise moment, I stumbled upon the fundamental notion that writing was the thing that made you feel less lonely.

Besides, ambition has always been, for me, simply the means by which one seeks revenge on inadequacy and general mediocrity.

Although I do distinctly recall that, one day as I walked alone down a sun-scorched path in amongst the artichokes, I felt someone walking alongside me – that shadowy peripheral figure again, that absent presence – and I think I might have stopped crying after that.

'*Toujours mes yeux las se réveillent à l'étoile d'argent...*'[29]

Predictable, I think, as my gaze now shifts towards the statue once more.

And there she is. Sitting nonchalantly at the base of the plinth, she reminds me of one of those Renaissance paintings of the devoted Magdalene in the shadow of the crucifixion. She

29   Always my weary eyes wake up to the silver star...

catches sight of me and waves. Awkwardly and without thinking, I wave back. I don't pause for a moment to reflect upon what she is doing there at eight o'clock in the morning or, indeed, how long she has been in that position. Instead, I simply accept the fact that she is there, and I quickly discover in myself that the overriding sensations are those of relief and gratitude.

There follows a fairly involved and frankly confusing pantomime of hand gestures, and I feel none the wiser at its conclusion. However, after getting dressed and making my way downstairs, I find she is sitting in the lobby of the hotel, waiting for me. She jumps to her feet in a manner that I flatter myself might be possible evidence of excitement. She reaches for my hand and kisses my cheek. I feel a shudder pass down my spine, which I ignore as much as I am able.

'Bonjour, *monsieur*. It is a beautiful day, yes?'

'Looks good,' I say as I wonder at what stage in our association, if ever, I might bring up the whole issue of the artichokes.

'You have not had breakfast yet, Monsieur Marc?'

'No, just a coffee in my room a little while ago.'

'Then, please, we go to the best place I know in Charleville for *our* breakfast.'

OK, I know the possessive pronoun as she actually spoke it doesn't really warrant italics – I just liked her use of the word and felt I wanted to draw your attention to it.

About fifteen minutes later, Madame Autry and I are sitting at a table outside a small but busy brassiere located on the Cours Briand, less than a stone's throw away from the relocated and ever watchful duke. The Cours Briand is a wide, tree-lined, largely commercial thoroughfare with definite aspirations to boulevardhood, which, ultimately, takes you out of Charleville and towards Mézières. As far as Rimbaud is concerned, and to the best of my knowledge, it takes no part in his story, so I have given it scant attention in the past. If pushed on the subject, I would go as far as to suggest it gives the impression of a late-nineteenth-century addition, perhaps reflecting the town's growing prosperity – but I could be wrong.

Our coffee and our croissants are pleasant enough, although not quite justifying the gushing superlatives that my companion in breakfast has recently been making on their behalf. But the waiter is friendly, and I did notice when we arrived that, behind the espresso machine, there is a small, framed copy of Picasso's sketch of the Carjat portrait. Anne, I notice, says very little as she is eating, but she smiles frequently at me, and I find myself reciprocating.

Eventually, as she brushes the crumbs from her mouth with her napkin, she asks me a single-word question: 'Rimbaud?'

I exhale loudly in what I hope is the universal vernacular for mild exasperation.

'Oh, *monsieur*, so did you not manage to do any more work last night?' she asks, sounding concerned as much as curious.

'Sort of,' I say, a reply that has the virtue of being an approximately honest one.

'I thought about your book too,' she adds in tones that might have, in a different era, passed as coquettish.

'Oh really?'

'Yes, it wasn't anything particularly earth-shattering, just that your reader is embarking on a journey with you, in terms of all sorts of meanings of that word – you know, geographically, psychologically, in a literary sense and in a kind of spiritual one too. The fact that you're arriving in Charleville on the very first page really helps impart that feeling.'

Although I do not recall ever having discussed the opening of my novel with her, there are several periods during the previous afternoon about which my memory is predictably a little vague. Besides, it isn't some jealously guarded formula, and the point she has just made is a perfectly valid one.

'Of course, in Rimbaud,' she continues, 'in both his poetry and his life, travel is so often a metaphor for spiritual and psychological transition. This, of course, goes all the way back to 'Le Bateau Ivre' and possibly even before that. So for your reader, a connection is made right at the beginning of your text.'

Unexpectedly, I feel very self-conscious, exposed and slightly vulnerable. Although, to my surprise, the feeling in this current context is not at all an unpleasant one. I take a long, measured, reflective sip of my café au lait. 'I hadn't actually thought of it in those terms,' I say, but I can think of nothing further to add.

'But you see, Charleville, this stupid little town right here, huh? It is my fucking stupid little town too! For so long, it remained the centre of his' – she struggles for the word – 'his web. His world kept expanding, but Charleville remained on its fixed, permanent axis. He ran away, but he always came back. Of course, he would have despised the whole concept – the whole notion of *home*.' She curls her lip and gives the word a sneering emphasis. 'Yet as late as 1887, he refers to himself in a letter written from Aden as a native of Charleville. It is true; you can look it up.'

'I'm sure you're right.'

Anne shakes her head reflectively. 'It is the biological compass of the human soul.'

I make a mental note to record that line a little later.

'You see, Marc, it is not a fashionable viewpoint, I understand, but I live in this town, and I know that, in his heart, Rimbaud was all Charleville! He always was. He had all his grand ideas and his ambitions, but they were often born out of the restrictions and the frustrations and the sense of containment he felt because he was here. So, even in that respect, whether you term it "anger" or "inspiration", there is no point denying that Charleville was so massively significant in Rimbaud's life. You can just imagine the sense of failure and disapproval he would have experienced returning here without the literary or material success he felt was his destiny. In a place like this, the shame of that would have been utterly unendurable.'

I brush a few stray croissant crumbs from my lap. 'I think you'll find that is pretty common in most small provincial towns.'

'No, no, Marc. There is nowhere like this place. Rimbaud was never writing from a solely creative impulse or from the sheer joy of actually writing; no, he wrote so that, ultimately, he would become a distinguished and successful writer and he could take his place amongst all the dignitaries of his home town on parade days. When he failed in this and couldn't cope with the shame of his own crumbling ambitions, he abandoned writing altogether in order to seek alternative success and personal status in other fields. That is not artistic integrity, *monsieur*, that is just fucking Charleville!' Her voice is now of sufficient volume and intensity that the couple sitting at an adjacent table turn and look awkwardly in our direction.

'I think,' I say, in what I hope might be judged to be a calm, reflective tone, 'that it is one factor rather than the sole factor.'

Anne leans across the table towards me, her eyes burning into mine. 'No, no. You don't understand. Look, I grew up here. I knew about Rimbaud. I saw his statue by the station, I walked past the museum and all that, but I didn't really know about his poetry until I was doing French literature in college. We had an amazing teacher who introduced his work to us. He had come from some small town in Brittany originally.'

I find myself fighting the urge to smile. 'Really?'

'He was in his fifties, maybe, and not far off retirement. He was gay too, but that wasn't any of our business. But he understood how Rimbaud might have suffered because of his sexuality in a close knit community like Charleville. He said he'd experienced similar attitudes when he was younger. His theory about Rimbaud abandoning poetry was linked to the shame and guilt the young poet felt, whenever he was back in his rigid and restricted hometown, about his homosexual relationship with Verlaine. To understand Rimbaud, he used to say, you must let him live in his own century. His verse may sound contemporary to our ears, but he lived amongst the bigotries and prejudices of the late nineteenth century. Indeed, as late as the 1940s, some biographers were only comfortable with the word "friendship" when referring to Rimbaud's association with Verlaine. He always used to remind us that there was no network in those days, and confined to Charleville, Rimbaud would have felt confused, angry and isolated. And linking his... perhaps, nowadays, we could say "self-loathing" and his poetic ambitions was what my teacher argued drove him to abandon literature. In Rimbaud's mind, the two aspects of his life were indivisible. By turning his back on one, he was, in effect, turning his back on both. Perhaps "denying" would be a better term...'

She looks at me possibly quizzically or possibly accusingly, but I say nothing.

'So,' she continues, 'the solution would be to become someone else and go somewhere else. Two *autres*! And he would never be recognised. Effectively, for the last sixteen years of his life, he was wearing a disguise.'

I think for a moment. 'It's a theory, I suppose. But it casts Verlaine entirely in the role of the seducer, and really I think Rimbaud was well aware of his friend's orientation before they actually met face to face. In fact, he actually sounds a little flirtatious in one of the earliest surviving letters.'

'But the fact remains that the only unequivocally documented gay relationship in Rimbaud's life was with Verlaine. Everything else is mainly rumour and conjecture.'

'I know, but it seems like a slightly simplistic reading of the situation.'

'He fucking killed himself.'

'Who did?'

'My teacher. The year after he retired.'

'Shit, that's terrible...'

'He was very depressed, they said. He loved teaching, and they shouldn't have let him retire...' Her voice trails off, and I wonder if she is tracing a memory or she has simply exhausted the subject.

Out of the blue, she opens her hand, spreading her fingers wide, and places it palm down next to mine on the table. She looks at me and then at our hands. 'Fuck!' she exclaims. 'Don't our hands look similar? Look! I hadn't noticed that before. I mean, fuck… Marc, they are virtually identical.'

13. Crossroads

At the conclusion of our breakfast, Anne informs me she is meeting a friend outside the branch of Carrefour City where I had first encountered her the previous day. I assume that, based on no evidence whatsoever, this friend is very probably male, but I volunteer to walk with her, and she seems happy to accept my offer.

We walk past the duke along Rue Pierre Bérégovoy.

Rimbaud was actually born on this street, when it was known as Rue Napoleon, and a small plaque on what was once number 12 commemorates this fact. I glance at it as we pass, but I feel not the slightest urge to make any sort of comment to my companion.

We are mainly walking at a fairly leisurely pace in what I would term an amiable silence. At one point, I glance towards her and catch her looking at her hand; she looks back at me and smiles. It is as though she has decided this is now a secret we both share. Although I would strongly doubt that her delight in the discovery would match my own for its intensity.

But as we now approach the left turn into Rue Bourbon, I hear the sound distinctly for the first time. (Rue Bourbon /

Bourbon Street – should I draw the reader's attention to this?) Just a guitar and a single voice, faintly at first, but as warm and familiar to me as memory itself.

I had woman in Jackson, had one in Tennessee

I look at Anne for a moment as my mouth contorts into an awkward and clumsy distant relative of a smile and then I concentrate on the music once more.

But my Gulf Coast woman keeps breakin' down on me

As we turn the corner, Anne and I see him for the first time, virtually simultaneously. He is standing at the entrance to Carrefour City – a slim, handsome man wearing an open white shirt and sporting a wide-brimmed fedora. As he sings, he accompanies himself on a wood-bodied National Resonator guitar.

Of course, I recognise him instantly.

Meanwhile, Anne is looking at me and frowning. This is obviously not the person she had the arrangement to meet. 'Is that who the fuck I think it is?'

I smile and mumble half-heartedly to myself. 'That is one steady rollin' man.'

'Yes, yes, I know that but what the fuck exactly is he doing on my spot? Come on.'

She walks quickly towards him, and I follow her.

As we draw near, he finishes his song. At which point, he smiles broadly, removes his hat and holds it out it towards us. 'I'm much obliged, boss; much obliged, ma'am…'

I turn to Anne. 'Errrm… boss? Really? Is he actually going to talk like this?'

She makes a face. 'Well, sadly, it is probably historically accurate.'

I suck air loudly through my teeth. 'It does jar a bit, though, doesn't it? It's all a bit, you know, *Porgy and Bess* and…'

Anne holds her hand up to silence me. 'Maybe you just need to get used to it.'

The fedora is once again proffered in our direction. 'Boss? Ma'am? Much obliged for your kindness...'

I incline my head as though about to impart a great confidence. 'Look, I don't know what you're doing here; I really don't,' I whisper as I drop a ten-euro note into his hat. 'I'm really not sure how this will fit with the overall narrative.'

'Much obliged, much obliged... Any 'ticular song y'all wanna hear? I got all sorts, man, I got...'

'You must leave now,' says Anne abruptly. 'This is my spot; you must go somewhere else.'

'Respectfully, ma'am. Name's Johnson, Robert Leroy Johnson, and I believe I be perfectly within my rights to be standin' just about right here now.'

I see a look of despair pass across Anne's face. '*What?* What do you mean?'

He smiles at her in a manner that teeters on the flirtatious. 'Well, ma'am, seems like I be fetched up at a place called Carrefour, is that right?'

'Yes, obviously; the name is written over the door!'

'So ma'am, tell me, what is *Carrefour* in English?'

'Crossroads.'

He lets out a dry, devilish chuckle. 'Well, ma'am,' he says, running his thumb with consideration around the brim of his fedora, 'where else would you expect to find Robert Johnson?'

This is possibly a very weak and tenuous transitional device, I think, but before I can consider its implications, Anne has started shouting again.

'For fuck's sake, really? I'm not in the mood for this right now. I'll see you later, Marc...'

And with that ringing in my ears, she turns and walks away back down Rue Bourbon.

'Whoa, whoa! Dat lady sure do seem to have got herself vexed 'bout somethin', boss.'

I pinch the bridge of my nose between my thumb and

forefinger. '*Boss*' is bad enough, but '*Dat?*', '*Vexed?*' Really?

'Look, I really have to say something here. This is not the way we do things any more. You just can't speak like this now. It's so not acceptable and utterly wrong on every possible level!'

'Maybe you's gotta start lettin' folk live in der own time, boss,' the bluesman says, narrowing his eyes and regarding me with suspicion. 'You see, I'm just a product of my time and my place. And that be 1920s, Hazlehurst, Robinsonville, Mississippi. Yes, sir. Can't do nuthin' 'bout dat, boss.'

'I'm sorry, but it feels that this whole thing is descending into stereotyping.'

With something I take to be mild disdain, he flicks his wrist at me. 'No, no... Look-a-here, makes no difference if y'all be playing music, paintin' pictures or writin' dose books. Accuracy is truth, man! It's honesty. Dat's da thing, right? Is what Son House, Patton, Blind Lemon... is what made 'em all great, right? They told the truth!' He breaks into a grin. 'But they not as great as me, of course! No, sir!'

I wince so vigorously at *Look-a-here* that I fear I may have lost the finer points of his argument.

'You see, dat's the most important thing, man. Y'all need to be tellin' the truth. Beauty is truth; truth, beauty. Mmmm, them such fine, fine words.'

I inhale sharply. 'Um, they're from Keats. I'm surprised you...'

'I know dey from Keats, man! 'Ode on a Grecian Urn'. Ya'll surprised I know Keats? Now who's talkin' 'bout stereotypes? Think a black man can't have hisself a little learnin'?'

'No, I just...'

He breaks into a low chuckle, although I feel I am the subject of amusement rather than mockery 'So, come on, man. What song do y'all wanna hear?'

I think for a moment and, avoiding what might be regarded as the most obvious requests, suggest instead one of my personal favourites.

He says nothing but simply plays an introductory guitar figure that is markedly different from the recorded version and then launches himself into the first verse. The tempo of the song too is vastly slower to the version I have known for forty years.

I'm a downhearted man and I ramble all night and day.

He sings beautifully, in a manner that could almost be regarded as plaintive.

I'm a downhearted man and I ramble all the night and day.

Then he closes his eyes and tilts his head back as he sings the concluding refrain.

But I can't find me no kind of rider in any old place I stay.

I watch his left hand and observe the comparative ease with which he plays such delicate, subtle guitar phrases. There is nothing simple or basic about this music – it is as intricate and obscure as anything you might find in any text by Rimbaud. But there is an even stronger connection that I acknowledge I have been guilty of overlooking up until this moment.

The parallels suddenly manifest themselves between the restless, nomadic, itinerant bluesman and the restless, nomadic, itinerant poet. Both artists seemed to be in a constant state of escape and flight during their periods of greatest artistic creativity. Rimbaud eventually succeeded in making himself absent from both the country of his birth and from poetry itself. Johnson, in many respects, given the scant biographical material available, went one stage further and appears sometimes to have actually been absent from his own life. Maybe this is why they have both held such a fascination for me for as long as I can remember.

I'm leaving in the morning might be heading east or west.

Maybe I once perceived genius to be the artist's consolation for being in a perpetual state of motion.

Absent, elsewhere and shining like an old, polished chrome bottleneck.

But gradually, I suppose, I am realising that Anne is right and Rimbaud had Charleville as one of the great constants in his life. This town was the point he journeyed from and the point against which he could measure his own progress. Even when it was being mocked or despised, it was always present. Present even when it was absent. Johnson had no such focal point in his life, just that relentless red road leading to the empty inn.

I'm leaving in the morning and I could head east or west.

I realise that my invented Fantasy Robert Johnson and my invented Fantasy Rimbaud probably say far more about me than I might wish. They inhabit a world without emotional restrictions or physical constraints, and having abandoned such traditional human comforts, they are free to pursue their own artistic objectives. Hardship and isolation are obvious and inevitable consequences, but even these can be refashioned as source material. By comparison, we are all mundane and unremarkable; our only talent is the capacity to recognise those precious few members of our own species who are not.

Anyone can gaze at a horizon – the real skill is gazing beyond it.

But them blues will always find me deep down in my distress.

A handful of vaguely inquisitive shoppers gather at a discreet distance and observe the curiously attired musician. But this extraordinary music that has changed so many lives doesn't seem to hold their attention particularly, and one by one, as the great Delta bluesman reaches the final turnaround of his song, they have all wandered off. I observe him as he watches them depart, but his face betrays no trace of emotion. However, I hear him murmuring something under his breath as – with a languid, feminine dexterity – he removes the bottleneck from the little finger of his left hand.

'That was beautiful,' I declare, mainly for the sake of breaking the silence. 'Thank you, Robert. May I call you Robert?'

'It's my name, man,' he says vaguely, without looking at me.

'Look, it's probably just the language thing – maybe they miss the sense of some of the lyrics.'

He replies initially with a wordless dismissive mumble. 'Well, I ain't fixin' to stay 'round these parts for long anyway. No, boss.'

'I ... I sort of guessed as much.'

He leans over suddenly and touches my arm. 'Maybe y'all can do one more thing for me, then. Like maybe dere's a place round dese parts where a travellin' man such as me could find hisself some company? Like a nice young lady. Or maybe there's somewhere I could find a little somethin' to soothe a poor man's throat?'

I shake my head slowly as I realise we are about to lapse into the stuff of tedious vernacular cliché and the general oral tradition of the blues. 'No, no, not this! Come on, just play us another song, Robert, please. 'Sweet Home Chicago': play that one; it's a classic. Everyone knows that. God, Barack Obama actually sang it in the White House!'

'Who?'

'The President of the United States.'

'Aw, come on, man... Why would da President wanna sing a black man's music?'

'Because... Oh, look, just sing the fucking song. I'll give you another twenty.'

Robert looks at me cautiously. 'OK, man. But after dis I'll need some refreshment, y'all catch what I'm sayin'?'

'Yeah, we can sort something out.' I watch him as he puts a capo on the second fret of his guitar and checks the tuning. It is now, I think; finally, this is the time I can ask the question. It's the question that has troubled me for decades. And it's nothing to do with any crossroads. Robert Johnson travelled extensively during his years as a working musician, often journeying far beyond his native Mississippi. According to some sources, he worked as far away as New York and even Canada.

'So, Robert?'

'What's up, man?'

'Hey, I've just got to know something. For someone like you, who travelled so much and visited so many places, why in 'Sweet Home Chicago' do you refer to Chicago as being in California?'

He frowns at me. 'Huh?'

'Was it some kind of joke?'

He smiles and shakes his head. 'No, man. It just fitted da metre of da song. It was kinda a damn good rhyme too. Don't youse people 'round here know nuthin' 'bout poetry?'

14. AUTRE

I would hesitate before using the words 'admire' or 'envy', but I do have a quiet, begrudging respect for any seasoned drinker who can walk into a supermarket and purchase alcohol at nine o'clock in the morning. I always think it requires a certain confidence or sense of swaggering purpose.

So here I am, in Carrefour again, buying a six pack of beer for Robert Johnson and filling my basket with as many useless additional items as I can find. Presumably, the fly spray, chewing gum and salad dressing will dissuade the lady at the checkout from jumping to any negative moral judgements. Mr Johnson, I imagine, in keeping with his own carefully curated mythology, would have probably preferred spirits, but I feel there is a line I'm not prepared to cross at this time of day. Besides, this particular brand of beer is deceptively potent – as I have very recently discovered myself.

Johnson, I recall, was known to have a fondness for hard liquor, or perhaps this is simply a cliché and another stereotype that has attached itself with comparative ease to the meticulously edited narrative of the musician's life – the same continually referenced morality fable that always threatens to claim and overwhelm the factual events. Rimbaud's life can be seen in much the same way. And by even thinking it or considering it, I am acknowledging it, and therefore I realise I am as guilty as anyone of perpetuating the same ridiculous subtext. Thus, the predictable and traditional mythology of all undiscovered artists is littered with stories of alcohol, drugs, promiscuity, poverty and rootlessness. The veracity of these anecdotes is not the issue; they must simply endorse the main themes of our expectations.

'Poor Bob,' I say under my breath as I pay for the beer.

I wander back out on to Rue Bourbon, but he is nowhere to be seen. I am both surprised and not surprised by this, and so I smile lopsidedly at no one in particular.

'Oh, he's gone then, I see,' says an indignant voice to my left, which I acknowledge with a shrug without feeling the need to turn towards it.

'Good fucking riddance...'

'That's hardly fair,' I retort, bristling very slightly.

Anne Autry now wanders over to where I'm standing and, without the slightest suggestion of subtlety, peers into my carrier bag at the six pack of beer. 'I do not know why he suddenly turned up like that. He is entirely superfluous to your narrative, Marc.'

I shake my head. 'I don't agree. I think there are some very interesting parallels with Rimbaud. Both as an artist and in my general perception of him.'

Anne removes the can of fly spray from my carrier bag. She looks at me and makes a face before putting the can back in the bag. 'No, no,' she says emphatically, 'you need to return to Rimbaud; this is distracting you from the main theme of your book.'

I raise my gaze above the rooftops opposite. 'Not you as well! Look, I think I am just exploring the same themes by using a different artist as an example.'

She looks at me sternly. 'But I feel that, with Aristotle and Yeats and now Robert Johnson, you are in danger of losing sight of your subject. He needs to remain the focus.'

'I don't think there is any—'

'How tall was he?' she asks abruptly. 'How tall was Rimbaud?'

I feel my eyebrows contort into a slight frown. 'That's a very curious question.'

'Not really; it's very simple. How tall was he?'

I think for a moment. 'Well, many of the biographies allude to the fact that he had a growth spurt in his late teens. And I suppose that, if you look at the photographs of him in Africa, he seems slim and quite tall. So I'd say five feet ten, maybe eleven.'

'He was five feet six.'

'Really?'

'Indeed he was. Quite short, I think, by today's standards.'

I stare at her blankly. 'Are you sure?'

'Of course I'm sure. He was definitely five feet six. I think it's actually in one of his letters somewhere.'

'I'm surprised; I had no idea he was—'

'No, of course. Rimbaud in your mind is tall and slim, but really, that is just another *autre* you have constructed. The truth is all there in the original documents. These multiple Rimbauds, of which yours is just one of so many, you must leave that behind now, Marc. Even when you can see how the life of the poet has been distorted, you only do so through your own distortions. It is just static on top of static. You need clarity. You need focus! Your Rimbaud is not the answer to your problems; it is not even the fucking answer to Rimbaud.'

Yesterday, her comments would have had little effect on me. Today, however, I find myself feeling strangely hurt by her remarks.

'I thought,' I say, in what I hope passes for a neutral tone, 'I was attempting to resolve this by introducing Robert Johnson into the narrative.'

'Oh, Marc,' she replies, and I detect – with some relief, even delight – the affection in her voice.

She now stands next to me and takes my arm. 'I do understand; I really do. But it's a very personal thing between you and Rimbaud, and to me, it only really works when you focus exclusively on your... what would you say? Your relationship, maybe?'

'*Merde!*'

Anne instinctively turns towards the voice. 'Oooh, look who's back! Hey, Shorty!'

'*Mendiante!*'

'Whatever...'

I smile but can think of nothing further to add.

Anne continues. 'Now you are both here, you need to understand this, Marc. This man, this Rimbaud, he is the voice of perpetual adolescence for generations of perpetual adolescents! It is true. He speaks on your behalf, and for all those who are just like you.'

'*À l'adolescent que je fus.*'[30]

'Exactly! You see, Marc, you are like so many of them who come here: you want to recapture some sense of yourself, some long-dead hope, some unfulfilled possibility, some forgotten promise. It's like a fire that has gone out inside you, but you insist on kicking over the ashes.'

'*La réalité étant trop épineuse pour mon grand caractère.*'[31]

Ignoring this second interruption, Anne continues, 'You must understand that this is not all about your mother or the state of your ridiculous country! It's just that terrible sense of emotional disconnection that occurs as we get older. It happens to all of us eventually; it's like we just drift out of touch with ourselves. We become no more than vague acquaintances of our true natures. And yes, at that moment, we are genuinely our

30 To the adolescent that I was.
31 The reality was too thorny for my great character.

own *autre*. You fight it at first – without even knowing it, you do things and you say things as you try to convince yourself that you are now the person you always hoped you would be. However, it is obvious that anything once connected to your youth is so far back in the past as to be irrelevant, but this now marks the end of any tangible or affectionate connection to it.'

The other voices fall silent now as I wait to find my own. I look at Anne and notice again the birthmark she has just below her elbow on her right arm. Like the tricky, twisted symmetry of her eyebrows, I love her physical idiosyncrasies – anything that assuages my natural mistrust of perfection. It makes her seem human and yet somehow beyond human. As though these random details harmonise with some ancient order of things. One that is unspoken, timeless and universal. And far beyond anything I could even conceive or imagine.

'*Ah! Que le temps vienne*
'*Où les cœurs s'éprennent...*'[32]

A shiver passes down my spine, but I manage to gather my thoughts eventually. 'I don't think it was ever my intention to write a critical biography – there are already far too many of those anyway – or some worthy essay deconstructing the main themes in *Les Illuminations*. My original idea was to write something personal and at least partially autobiographical...'

Anne now grips my arm tighter. 'I understand, Marc, but you mustn't let yourself become distracted; you must write about Rimbaud and how he relates to your universal human themes, such as love and pain and regret and belief. You mustn't just immerse yourself in anecdotal nostalgia. That is so often the problem with *perpetual adolescents*. You spend far too long refusing to accept that you cannot effectively self-medicate by simply longing for your own youth.'

'*O journées enfants! — le corps un trésor à prodiguer.*'[33]

---

32 Ah, let the time come when hearts fall in love.
33 O childhood days! The body a treasure to be lavished.

Madame Autry instantly narrows her eyes and gazes in the direction of the voice. Her mouth contorts into a pout, and then surprisingly and very subtly, she begins to nod her head.

She then turns towards me.

Of course, in a sense, she is entirely right in what she is saying, but I feel she might be oversimplifying the issue somewhat. I was actually well out of my teens before I fully immersed myself in my obsession with Rimbaud, so the association with my youth is tentative at best. I have always returned to his work at times of stress and turmoil, and it remains one of the great constants in my life. I'm sure the connection with adolescence is in there somewhere, but it is possibly far more nebulous than Anne might be suggesting.

To me, Rimbaud has always been equally the voice of the frustrated and the ostracised. His is the perspective of the emotionally exiled and the spiritually isolated, and those are the aspects of his work with which I've always felt the greatest affinity. Evidently, these might be characteristics we associate with turbulent teenagers, but in my experience, they rarely cease as one matures. They remain in the minds of so many, connected in some way to traditional youthful dysfunction, and are probably regarded as natural or even healthy nowadays.

In some ways, I should point out that this very tradition seems traceable right back to Rimbaud, but no further than that. Rebellion is not simply the intentional denial of established ideas – any nihilistic fool can do that – it is often just an inadvertent consequence of an attempt to create new forms or new alternatives. Denial, therefore, is part of the creative drive, but it is also considered a rebellious stance. Rimbaud remains mired in that confusion. Destroying the past, in our eyes, is bold and honourable, but it is often wholly accidental. Countering this attitude, I realise awkwardly, is our tendency to lapse into nostalgia, and now I am looking guiltily at Anne.

She is making a face at me, and I smile at her. And somewhere in a book that I will never write or even have the skill to write are the following lines:

I loved her because she made the world available to me through my senses.

She taught me how to gaze at things in fear and wonder; she allowed me to feel an excitement that was unconditional and a joy that was unfettered.

In short, I loved her because she made me feel like a child.

15. Pan

And there it is.

Finally.

The line that gives me my connection.

You little fucking beauty!

A single line, but it is all I wanted.

Eleven words, in which I find all the justification I need to continue.

The smile is self-satisfied, even teetering on the smug, but my face seems genuinely incapable of any sort of alternative at present.

I knew I had to find something. It had been at the back of my mind since the previous evening, and I knew that I urgently needed to locate a reference in the original text. One that would connect my ideas to Rimbaud's.

And there it was!

In fucking *Les Illuminations* too!

Which, I feel, to be honest, gives it even greater authority and resonance!

In the poem 'Antique', Rimbaud writes about the Greek god

Pan, and at one point, he explicitly references the fact that Pan was a hermaphrodite. The line in French is 'T*on cœur bat dans ce ventre où dort le double sexe*' which translates as 'your heart beats in the belly where sleeps the double sex'.

Double sex!

The expression is perfectly unequivocal, and I don't think that Rimbaud could make his point any clearer. There were other more-ambiguous references dotted around a few of his other poems, but nothing as singularly overt as the line in 'Antique'.

The conversation with Anne a short while ago had reached a sort of natural conclusion, or else she had simply run out of the prerequisite enthusiasm for the subject. Whilst I felt that, at some point, I may need to digest and process what she had told me, I knew I had more pressing concerns. To this end, I left her outside Carrefour, promising that I would return, and then I'd immediately started walking briskly back to the Hôtel Couleurs Sud.

Within an hour or so of reading through the original French versions and the English translations, I'd stumbled upon the quote. It was a moment of vindication and a moment to cherish.

But now, I think, comes the difficult part.

Before he became our fabulous iconic vagrant poet, it is worth recalling that Rimbaud had been a precocious, brilliant and prize-winning pupil at the Collège de Charleville, who'd won accolades and awards for his Latin compositions in verse. As a student, he had made a meticulous study of the history of poetry and literature in general. Indeed, in the Lettre du Voyant, he summarises and theorises a great deal on poetic traditions as far back as ancient Greek literature.

So now I hesitate.

Yet if I am to speculate, I must only do so within the strictest realms of probability. However, I do find it almost impossible that, given his scholarly and academic background, Rimbaud was not well acquainted with Aristotle's teachings. Therefore, one can presume he was also aware of Aristotle's idea that the consciousness preceding birth was asexual, simultaneously both male and female and that specific genders were only made manifest at birth.

Was this what he was alluding to in 'Antique'? Maybe the 'double sex' is not sleeping in the conventional sense but simply dormant or inactive. (A recent translation actually uses the phrase 'lies still'.) A passive awareness of an ancient instinct encoded deep within our basic humanity. It sleeps within all of us. Actually, according to Rimbaud, in the belly. Interestingly, the word '*ventre*' can also be translated as 'womb', and I think Rimbaud was well aware of the ambiguity at work here. Again, this would serve to reinforce the idea that Pan was hermaphroditic.

This is the moment I finally look up from my books and wander over to the window. Perhaps seeking confirmation or vindication, I gaze out over the square, towards the bust, but the voice I hear is not the one I am expecting.

'I'm sorry, darling, but some of this does seem to be coming across more like conspiracy theory than literary criticism.'

I feel instantly the small, familiar contraction in the muscles at the back of my neck. 'Thanks, Mum; that's helpful, thanks. Always knew I could rely on you.'

'Oh come on now! You know I've always had the greatest respect for everything you've ever written. I just don't think this is the most productive use for your talents.'

'As I keep telling you, it's just an idea. Besides, you know how I write. It still very much conforms to the Cary Grant principle.'

'To the what?'

'Well, I say Cary Grant, but I'm not entirely sure that it is Cary Grant, to be honest. It's probably just some generic comedy staple. Anyway, there is this character, who might be Cary Grant, and he's attempting to avoid detection or capture in a city centre whilst a marathon or some long-distance race is being run. So, our character cunningly strips down to his vest and boxers and jogs alongside the runners, eventually blending in so well that he gives his pursuers the slip. That's basically how I have always written. I sort of jog alongside an idea for a while – aware of it, but not actively involved with it. But then I get slowly pulled into it and gradually absorbed by it, whether I want to be or not. I have absolutely no business being there, but after a while, nobody seems to know or to care.'

'Oh, right...'

'So, you see, it's just something I may wish to explore.'

'Well, I think it's fairly obvious what you really want to explore at the moment...' Her remark is nebulous yet pointed, and her recent demise has in no way impeded her rare gifts in this regard.

'What?'

'It doesn't matter,' she says predictably, in her usual hurried, dismissive tones. 'But I really do think you need to forget about all these other *distractions*.' She infuses the word with a frankly enviable contempt, the implication being that there is no need for her to be any more specific.

'They are just ideas, Mum, that's all.'

'I know, darling, but they're a bit off the subject, don't you think? And I know you don't want to hear this, but that silly woman sounds like she's been filling your head with all sorts of things.'

'Oh please!'

'It needs to be said, darling; sorry and all that...'

'She's a very intelligent woman, actually,' I say instinctively – sadly, with almost no conviction whatsoever.

'I see. Then I wonder why she hasn't actually got a job of any description and she is in fact a, you know, a...'

'*Mendiante*.'

'Oh, thank you again, young man.'

'Look,' I declare, attempting to regain control of the conversation. 'It's just an idea I was playing with and nothing more than that. OK, I admit it was sparked by something Anne said, but really, it is only idle speculation.'

'So what is the precise nature of this *speculation*?' The dreaded emphasis is back.

This is not going to be easy. I am trying to force a whole collection of random and very possibly misguided thoughts into some sort of order. I look out of my window over the square and, for a moment, I let my gaze fall on the reassuringly unambiguous railway station in the distance.

'OK, Mum, if one accommodates, even very broadly, Aristotle's idea that we are the descendants of hermaph—'

'Oh God, really? Not all this again!'

My neck muscles tighten once more, but I continue unperturbed, emboldened even. 'If, as I say, we are descendants of hermaphrodites, then surely we should be able to discover some trait or some aspects of human behaviour that could be judged a natural consequence of this? that doesn't seem outlandish or conspiratorial, does it?'

'If you say so, darling.'

'OK, consider something as primal as the sex drive. Approached from a slightly different angle, the desire for copulation could be regarded not as a basic instinct to procreate but as an evolutionary echo of a much more subtle sublimated urge to conjoin – to forge a union – with someone who represents your perfect other, or in Rimbaud's words, your *autre*.'

'Perhaps, you need to—'

'Maybe, just maybe, what remains in us buried in what we think of as lust, and desire is the faintest trace of that original need. A weak, diluted parody now, a tribute almost, but a connection nonetheless.'

'Oh, darling, that's just silly...'

I ignore the interruption. 'This primal, original instinct to conjoin, to unite, still sleeps in all our bellies!'

'If you say so.'

'As does the desperate and mathematically improbable urge to locate our true Aristotelian *autre*.'

She pauses for a moment, but evidently, not to digest the implications of what I have just told her. 'Is this what your new lady friend has been telling you?'

I shake my head, as I feel I am now reaching the point beyond which I will make no further tangible contribution to the conversation. 'No, well, she might have mentioned something, but I don't know if that qualifies as actually relevant.'

'Oh, darling, of course it's relevant. Perhaps this is the book that she should be writing and not you! Look, I think I said before that you really need to stay focussed on the original main themes and ideas of your book. Of course I understand; I am your mother and I know how tempting it must be, but you mustn't let yourself be led astray. Seriously, you need to remain engaged and involved with Rimbaud and not allow yourself to be diverted by what really amounts to little more than adolescent silliness.'

'Of course it's all about Rimbaud!' I say, my patience finally at breaking point. 'Rimbaud's quest was ultimately the pursuit of the unknown (*l'inconnu*); it's the central theme of his great poetic manifesto. It's not about revisiting old ideas or reshuffling somebody else's work. It's about whatever lies just beyond the scope of our comprehension. His theories may have appeared perverse or ridiculous to some, but Rimbaud's work was always about challenging conventional or established ways of thinking. Nothing was off limits to him; nothing was sacred or absolute.'

I turn around, but there is nobody there.

Just my books lying open on the bed.

But now there is the sound of music drifting in through the open window.

Once again, the voice is intimate, personal, pure and perfect, and it demands the attention of the listener.

Or at least it demands mine.

My momma she died and left me but she done the best she could.

'Too soon, too soon…'

My momma she died and left me but she done the best she could.

I wander over to the window and peer over the balcony at the street below my room. And there he is again. That 'Drunken Hearted Man'.

But those lowdown cheatin' women never mean a man no good.

'Hey, Robert,' I call, leaning out of my window at the conclusion of the song.

He turns around, removing his hat and craning his neck to look up at me. 'Hey, boss…'

'That was just beautiful, man. I always loved that song.'

'Much obliged, I'm sure,' he replies, offering his upturned hat once again for my inspection.

'Oh, right. Hang on; I'll come down.'

Less than a minute later, I am pushing open the glass-panelled entrance doors of Hôtel Couleurs Sud and stepping onto the street outside. I am carrying a crumpled twenty-euro note in my hand.

'Is that for me?' The voice is familiar but uncharacteristically excited and cheerful. 'Oh, that's very generous of you, Marc.'

I mask my surprise bizarrely by attempting to register exaggerated or even greater surprise.

'Anne?'

'Hello again…' she says, smiling.

'Where did…? What happened to Robert? He was here a few moments ago.'

'Oh, oh… he had to go. He had to be somewhere. He said to say goodbye.'

I look at her suspiciously. 'Did you send him away again, Anne?'

'No, *monsieur*. Well, maybe… just a bit.'

I put my hand on my forehead and run my fingers through my hair. I do this whilst I mutter to myself mutant expletives that are largely composed of random syllables from better known and more traditional obscenities.

'But Anne,' I say by way of weary conclusion, 'what was it this time, for fuck's sake?'

'Simple. I have to talk to you, and he was getting in my way,' she explains in her customary brutal tones.

'But why? What could be so important?'

'It is you, Marc.'

'What?'

'You are fucking up really badly; really *very* badly.'

'*Que comprendre à ma parole?*

'*Il fait qu'elle fuie et vole!*'[34]

She turns on her heel and points accusingly at the bust of Rimbaud. 'Not now, boy. You can have your say later.'

'*Mendiante!*'

She hisses back at him.

'So how am I fucking up?' I ask as she turns to face me.

'It is your book. You are looking too hard for something and, always, you are missing the most obvious. It's almost like you are trying to be too clever all the time. Too subtle, perhaps.'

'I don't know what you mean,' I say, genuinely puzzled by her remark.

'You were looking for allusions, quotes to back up your ideas about Aristotle, right?'

'Yes, I was.' I sound more defensive than I would have wished. 'And I found one too.'

'Yes, you found something, but you missed the most obvious reference. The most important one.'

More out of confusion then denial, I shake my head. 'No, I think what I found was—'

---

34 Who can understand my words? They flee and fly away

'No, Marc; no. You are wrong.' She lets out a sigh that makes her sound vaguely adolescent. 'OK, what is the only book that Rimbaud actually published in his lifetime?'

'*Une Saison en Enfer*, obviously.'

'A book that he oversaw before publication and even proofread. So everything in that book is, we can presume, just how he wanted it to be.'

'Probably, yeah.'

'This wasn't something hand-copied or recalled by Verlaine, Germain Nouveau or whoever from a missing original, like so many of the other poems. These are indisputably Rimbaud's words as he intended them to be read.'

'Of course.'

'So, Marc, what's the very final line of the work? The very final line in the only book that he ever published? A line that, following his instructions, was italicised in the original text?'

'Um...' I hesitate for a moment. 'Something about "*l'enfer des femmes*", the hell of women?'

'No, it's the line that follows that. He writes "et il me sera loisible de" and then in the original text he switches to italics to conclude "*posséder la vérité dans une âme et un corps*". Obviously, it is his intention to give it a clear emphasis.'

I recall the translation from memory: 'And it will be possible to possess the truth in one soul and one body.'

'So, do you actually think he could make it more explicit? Even more obvious for you?'

I look at her, but I say nothing. Partly, I am angry with myself for missing the quote. I hear the mocking laughter of the adolescent poet as the Place de la Gare, the Hôtel Couleurs Sud and the Bar de l'Univers all swim around me and my stupidity, whilst I remain its static eternal vortex.

After a moment or two, which I successfully elongate into a lifetime, she smiles sympathetically at me.

Then, suddenly, right there in the bright sun of this summer morning and without warning, there is another line from the book that I will never write:

Even the simple act of casting a shadow,
We will do for evermore in the light of the stars we have made.

16. ASSASSINS

Of course, the actual principle of taking a single idea from Rimbaud and extrapolating and inflating it into an entire thesis or even a philosophy is not without precedent. In fact, for close on a century now, it would appear to be virtually mandatory. There have been those who have focussed exclusively on his sexual orientation, his absent father, his political viewpoints, his abandonment/rejection of literature, his suggested interest in the occult and, inevitably, his relationship with his mother.

In common, just like Rimbaud, we are all desperately attempting to run a golden chain from star to star in pursuit of that one huge, final, dazzling revelation.

Rimbaud gives that shift between late adolescence and adulthood a cultural and moral gravitas, together with the power that allows us to invest the poetry with an almost didactic nobility. Apart from that, the preoccupations of that whole period, certainly in my experience, can be defined simply as:

1) Music to Wear Clothes To.
2) Sex.
3) Clothes To Listen To Music In.

135

There might be other more nuanced aspects, but I suspect they might have passed me by or I have probably just forgotten them. If I had any grand desire to change the world, it was only insofar as it might better serve my own personal needs (see 1 to 3 above).

So, it is customary to place Rimbaud, during his most creative period, at the transitional point between childhood and maturity, between tradition and radicalism, and between conformity and rebellion. It is thus every tale ever told by a teenager in revolt, at the precise moment of breaking free, with all the attendant fear and passion.

It is a seductive rather than entirely robust theory, and I realise that, as I gather together and attempt to roughly assemble these thoughts, I am probably echoing the very sentiments Anne expressed about me earlier.

But the more I think about it, the more I think that Rimbaud should be a verb.

To rimbaud.

Whether in art or in life, its meaning would be obvious and universal: to stand in youthful and noble opposition to established ideas; to challenge the whims of an outdated, distant or failing authority; to follow your own calling, even if it means self-denial and suffering; but also to achieve all this not by simply negating the past but by establishing brilliant new alternatives.

Yes, I rimbaud, you rimbaud, we rimbaud…

I never went back home and never went back to school because I was rimbauding.

I was brilliant back in the day; I truly was. God, you should have seen me rimbaud.

Didn't he rimbaud?

He rimbauded.

Rimbauded 'til the butcher cut him down…

Personally, I might well be suspicious of any man who had never rimbauded.

Nothing to be ashamed of, lad, all perfectly natural…

'*Voici les temps des assassins*,' says the voice from Place de la Gare, and for once, there is no counterargument. Now is the time of the assassins.

The line that concludes the poem 'Matinée d'Ivresse' in *Les Illuminations* remains one of the greatest slogans to be found in nineteenth-century French literature and the one line of Rimbaud's with which many people are familiar. It is a protest song in seven words. It is simultaneously a call to arms and a *cri de cœur*, spray-painted over decaying walls and across infinite skies. It is urgent and primal, and it also looks really good hand-stencilled onto a T-shirt across a screen-printed image of Margaret Thatcher.

Well, it does when you are twenty-two.

And on this subject, I do speak from experience.

But being Rimbaud, nothing is straightforward, and even this simple phrase is wide open to multiple interpretations. It has generally been thought that Rimbaud was using the word 'assassin' in its original sense, derived from the Arabic word '*haschischin*', which relates to the murderous cultists of eleventh-century Cairo, who smoked hashish as it nullified any awareness of pain or death. Rimbaud was known to have smoked opium, and given that the poem is about intoxication, there is a sound logic to this interpretation.

However, in the poem 'Conte', also in *Les Illuminations* and thus written very roughly during the same period, Rimbaud uses the verb form of assassin to describe a murder. So it is equally likely he was using assassin in the sense that we understand the word today.

And, of course, it gave Henry Miller the title for his book about Rimbaud.

Which is quite possibly unforgivable.

It is not that I don't like Henry Miller – admittedly, I have never liked his book about Rimbaud – but in all honesty, I rather enjoy the continuity of my irrational mistrust and suspicion. I feel the same about foot spas, courgettes, Led Zeppelin and Tunbridge Wells.

I smile to myself again.

Since Anne brought to my attention about ten minutes ago the relevance of the final line in Rimbaud's sole published book, I have succumbed to a sort of uncharacteristic and slightly manic optimism. I can't help feeling that the connection Anne made between my theme and Rimbaud is also a connection between Anne and me. I am aware this is the kind of idea that functions better when unarticulated, yet it is one I feel most acutely.

On account of her vital contribution, my project has, I feel, just become *our* project, and I find that this is yet another cause to smile.

After announcing that she had to be somewhere else, we had said our farewells a few minutes ago, and I had watched her strolling so casually and so brilliantly up Avenue Jean Jaures, back towards the centre of town. Meanwhile, I bumbled and lumbered my way back to my room and began rereading 'Adieu', the final chapter in *Une Saison en Enfer*.

I have always shied away from the whole notion of confidence, perhaps because, for many years, it has so rarely been an option available to me. But suddenly, I find now that, with very little effort, I am able to envisage some of these ideas translating quite easily into book form. I would still incorporate my own story, so there would remain a strong autobiographical element, but that shouldn't detract too much from Rimbaud and the chief themes of the book.

Of course, the book would have to feature Anne at its core, its focus and its absolute epicentre. In fact, without Anne, there would not be a book at all.

And now I'm thinking about her again – thinking how she would probably laugh at me or brush away any suggestion that she may have made any tangible contribution. Whether this stems from simple modesty or a reluctance to form any sort of attachment, I am in no position, from the short time I have known her, to judge with any accuracy. However, I can picture the dismissive hand gesture and the facial grimace indicating an apparent and deep abiding disinterest in the subject.

Nonetheless, I am not fooled; it is simply a device, I imagine, to discourage any further enquiry.

Now my mind is suddenly elsewhere, and I find I am fanning my fingers out on the bed in front of me as I recall what she'd said earlier about our hands being so alike. '*Identical*', I believe, was the word she used. I narrow my eyes and extend my arm, perhaps aiming for greater objectivity. Identical, I think, might be over stressing the point, but I would concede that there was indeed a strong, immediately obvious resemblance – in particular, the proportions of the fingers and the particular angle of the thumb. However, this was, I confess, of less interest to me than the fact that she'd actually noticed the similarity in the first place. To me, this would seem to imply a degree of attention, of scrutiny and, perhaps, even of interest.

Not so much at the time, but it now seems like a significant moment. Perhaps another tiny axis around which my world and my life would one day shift. A page torn from the *Story of Us*, it would perhaps be a moment loaded with prescience and meaning. Rimbaud brought her to me and then, in return, she revealed to me the greatest truth about Rimbaud. And there is nothing else at this moment that seems to be of any greater consequence.

Yes, once I rimbauded; I rimbauded every place I set foot. I rimbauded in and out of situations, out of lives and locations. I rimbauded without respite, and without rhyme or reason. I rimbauded from dusk 'til dawn, from season to season, but now, Anne, no more will I rimbaud.

The figure that dwelt in shadows, the presence by my side, and the hand that gripped mine in the darkness and at those times of greatest need and saved me from the descent into madness.

She has returned to me.

If my life had no purpose beyond the hope
And the anticipation of our next reunion,
Then it would surely have purpose enough.

17. ANNE

'Fuck, have you any idea how much I've been dreading that question? Mainly, I think, because I'm not sure if there's a single way I can answer it with any accuracy!'

'But the thing with Marc, I think, is that he really has such a narrow perspective on Rimbaud. Perhaps too narrow. And I know he'll absolutely hate me for saying this, but for him, it all seems to be so tied up with nostalgia – to such an extent that the two are virtually inseparable. It is ultimately little beyond a yearning for the certainties of his youth, for those simple choices and all too self-evident truths. It is therefore hard for him to separate that emotional connection from the actual poetry of Rimbaud. I fear that this is a common problem. There is no cult of Rimbaud, not any more, even if there ever was. There are just those lost people – the social and emotional refugees of all generations – who drift into Rimbaud's orbit and who, one day, make that inevitable trip to Charleville, as though it offers them the chance to revisit a purer, less corrupted version of the world and of themselves. So, initially, I felt that Marc was in some ways fairly true to this type. He was middle-aged, disillusioned, and evidently trying to reconnect with a more vibrant and essential aspect of himself through his love of Rimbaud and what Rimbaud represented to him. Although, I feel he perhaps let himself become too focussed on the latter aspect.'

'The strange thing is that I don't actually regard Marc as a particularly attractive man. Certainly not in the conventional sense. Or in any sense, really. Yet I find there is something oddly compelling about him. I feel like I have known him all my life; it is as though he reminds me of so many people and yet of no one person in particular. He manages to convey the idea that he is not fully formed somehow; like he's going through some amazing life-changing process, but thus far, he has only reached its mid-point. I imagine he has been in precisely that same state for a great many years. But at other times, I only sense the sadness, and I see him as that final flickering of irrational, desperate hope before it is all extinguished and all is dark.'

'Yet despite all that, I do find myself strangely drawn to him. He is not the sort of person who strikes me as weak or needy, yet I find I have this strange – and I must say, uncharacteristic – urge to protect him. To save him from having to confront his own failings and disappointments. Similarly, there is nothing in his manner or conversation that specifically suggests he is lonely, yet something compels me to make sure he has company as much as possible.'

'In some respects, I suppose, some of his ideas and his particular way of thinking are not all that dissimilar to my own. Although, ironically perhaps, I do genuinely doubt that we'll ever be in perfect accord about Rimbaud! But I do share a certain interest in that theory about hermaphroditic ancestors. I had a teacher a long time ago, a fabulous lady, who took us for classics and psychology and was thus able to introduce me to both Freud and Aristotle. She also speculated on more than one occasion that the sex drive and impulse to procreate was an evolutionary echo of some sort of original desire to conjoin.

To literally seek reunion. As she put it, the urge to penetrate was simply the shadow cast by an ancient need to recombine. She cited as evidence the fact that, as a species, human beings naturally and instinctively perform the act of sex face to face when there are better and possibly more effective ways of guaranteeing impregnation.'

'In fact, she got into quite a bit of trouble one term on account of one of her slightly more extreme ideas. It was, as I recall, quite a scandal at the time, and I think I'm right in saying that she was actually suspended. Of course, it was a Roman Catholic school, and in the process, she upset a lot of the other teachers and a few parents as well. Her slightly, shall we say, progressive views usually guaranteed a degree of controversy, but on this one occasion, it was generally agreed she had taken things a little too far. To be fair, I think it's widely accepted nowadays that certain Christian sacraments were actually adapted from older pagan or polytheistic religions. But during one notable lesson, she went as far as to claim that the Eucharist, the taking of communion, was little more than a ritualised and symbolic homage – an acknowledgement of that same ancient yearning to seek the perfect union of two bodies. In effect, the mutual desire of two individuals to effectively fuse with each other. Specifically, in the case of the Eucharist, she claimed that the taking of the host was the means by which one body was taken entirely into another. As she pointed out, even the line, 'We are one body', is repeated by the congregation as the bread is being broken! Truthfully now, I think it was this latter comment that was the final insult and blasphemy! What happened next was swift and inevitable, but from that day forth, her lesson plans were much more closely scrutinised. And they suffered greatly, I believe, as a result. But I always felt that I owe her a great debt, and if nothing else, she gave me the courage and the confidence to trust my own instincts sometimes.'

'But to get back to Marc, I admit I probably spend far too much time thinking about him and what motivates him, and when a person occupies your thoughts like that, intentionally or otherwise, one develops an affinity, perhaps even something akin to that strange sense of *connectedness* that he refers to. I do feel I've now lost almost all objectivity when I think about him. It's like he's burrowed himself somewhere deep inside me – somewhere dark, nameless and utterly unknown to me – and I gradually lose the ability to think dispassionately or rationally. To be truthful, I find that, when I think about him, I bypass all intellectual functioning and rely on something that feels like pure instinct, which is comparatively unusual for me. Then what matters to me in this situation is what I feel rather than what I think, and if only in that respect, this is proving to be a fairly liberating experience for me.'

'I think I'm trying to avoid saying that I can identify and, yes, even sympathise with a lot of his feelings. I know it's probably silly, and the whole idea of the '*autre*' is something I would normally dismiss without a second thought, yet I do find that it fairly accurately describes certain aspects of our association. Even in the relatively brief time we have spent together. And I do understand that you sometimes have to take some liberties with certain factual realities for the sake of a good narrative.'

'I feel there is a subtle but definite strength of character about Marc; it's quite deceptive, and it may not initially be evident. But there is a strong sense of focus in his life that manifests itself in moments of reluctant enthusiasm. These are those times when he reveals the most about himself, entirely unintentionally. Apart from his mother, who remains a constant factor in his life even in death, he rarely mentions his family or if he has a wife or children. All of which suggests that he views Charleville and its association with Rimbaud as some sort of psychological and spiritual system restore. A reset button back to a time before life divided itself into happy and not so happy, fulfilled and unfulfilled, and managing and not managing very well, and it was just simply there all the time, disguised as possibility and opportunity. Who would not wish to revisit that? And I envy him that very simplicity of thought and deed. I think he genuinely believes he can recreate himself on the streets where Rimbaud walked and that he can find the formula. It is not lost; it is simply hidden! In the laboratory of the human soul, they whisper still of alchemy.'

'It is the most beautiful of all human conceits.'

'It is also the most inessential.'

'To be honest, I do rather enjoy the fact that Marc is confused and, generally speaking, lacks a certain level of commitment and conviction. I think this makes him rather more susceptible to unconventional ideas. I'm positive he would never go so far as to actually compare himself to Yeats, but I think he feels a certain admiration and empathy with the great poet's accommodation of the irrational and his famously open-minded attitude – which is something entirely different to his more obsessive and unconditional love for Rimbaud. In fact, I think that's pretty much, on the whole, the key to Marc's approach. When you find the dogmatic, orthodox interpretations wanting in some way, it makes sense to explore the unorthodox ones.'

'And even though he is noticeably reticent on the subject, Marc is definitely someone I would judge to be non-academic, and so I guess we can assume he is largely self-educated. Thus, I imagine, in his rare self-assured moments, he regards himself as more open-minded perhaps. And he possibly views this as tantamount to some sort of literary licence. I am virtually certain very few critics and biographers would give any sort of credence to Marc's speculations, but it's a fairly safe bet he would probably regard that as the strongest recommendation of all! His naiveté allows him a level of freedom and independence from conventional analyses. My instinct is that he would claim to be chasing after truth or knowledge, but like so many, I suspect he is simply in pursuit of a vague sense of purpose in his life.

His undoubted passion, regardless of its validity, is something I would genuinely envy, which should in turn prevent me from ever feeling remotely sorry for him.'

'Of course, his actual construct of Rimbaud, like his fantasy about Robert Johnson, is just another manifestation of his need to relate to this so-called '*autre*' on some level. Ultimately, I imagine it is in some way a quest for vindication or atonement. I can easily accommodate the idea that both artists represent the non-reductive nature of true genius, being those rare talents whose gifts transcend their sources and their influences and seek instead to trade in *l'inconnu* – the unknown. Those who take us on a journey that, ultimately, has neither starting point nor destination. Both also embody the idea of transience, motion and exile – in effect, *absence*, as being a sort of heroic cause essential for the creative mind.'

'But on a more personal level, the idea of the *autre*, I think, represents to Marc something like his vision of the ultimate human union. The eternal centre and the apex of all our earthly vanities. Something pure and moral and far beyond the chaos and carnage of this vile race of libidinous swine. However, the underlying arrogance of creating entirely new forms and new expressions sits on a straight and very narrow line that runs inevitably right back to Rimbaud.'

'There's that great line in 'Parade', in *Les Illuminations*: "*J'ai seul la clef de cette parade sauvage*", I alone have the key to this savage parade. That always makes me think of Marc.'

'Loving Marc is not an emotion, it is a fucking vocation – a solemn undertaking – and one feels sometimes that anyone wishing to apply should be given a medical and a reading list and be forced to sign all manner of disclaimers in advance. Of course, the truth is that I am in no way different myself and identical charges could be made against me!'

'Love is far too revealing an emotion to be displayed openly to the unworthy or the inadequately prepared!'

18. Words

It is late morning now, and the sun is hot as I amble back towards the Place Ducale in the hope of running into Anne again. I have left my jacket back at the hotel, and I'm rolling up the sleeves of my shirt as I walk. In doing so, I notice the birthmark I have near the elbow of my left arm, but I make no further comment on this.

Instead I force myself to concentrate on a recently published article about Rimbaud I have just read online. It was an attempt to deconstruct the myths by the time-honoured process of establishing counter-myths. In literature, this is not something that is even remotely exclusive to Rimbaud, yet it does seem to have been a fairly constant factor in the study of the poet this past century.

Again, I suspect that the ultimate urge for complete artistic understanding is little more than that same sublimated quest for sole ownership.

The article in question was a fairly sustained and, at times, predictable attack on Rimbaud's literary reputation, claiming that his status was entirely ill-deserved. It listed amongst his crimes the fact that his talent was never fully realised and even his very finest work was that of an immature and unworldly adolescent. Naturally, the writer cited various examples to support his theory, including the fact that Rimbaud was prone to overusing exclamation marks. He is certainly not incorrect in this. In the 'Vierge Folle' chapter in *Une Saison en Enfer*, which runs to a little under 1,500 words, Rimbaud inserts thirty-five exclamation marks – one for every forty-three words.

However, such aberrations are not specific to Rimbaud, as writers throughout history have taken liberties with grammatical rules and used punctuation for dramatic and narrative effect. Although I can't quite shake myself free of the lingering doubt that this particular writer was actually implying Rimbaud was demonstrating his poetic naiveté by his use of the same textual mannerisms we nowadays associate with every sulky, self-dramatising teenager we have ever known.

Or been.

Arthur Rimbaud (1854–1891): eternity's teenager.

(And once again it's impossible to avoid the implication that the clairvoyant gifts of Charleville's most famous son remain as impressive as ever.)

Of course, I realise that, by picking holes in the writer's notion about exclamation marks, I am by extension casting doubt on his entire premise. If that particular theory is invalid, why should we give any greater credence to his more generalised critique of Rimbaud? This, I appreciate, is not the soundest argument. In fact, it's not really an argument at all – it's more like a desperate attempt to discredit a witness. It's a dirty barrister's trick, and I shouldn't succumb to such tactics, but when it comes to Rimbaud, I find I still exhibit a strange, worryingly non-objective loyalty.

And with that loyalty comes a certain automatic defensiveness, out of which I do not seem capable of growing.

I now see Anne in the distance, and I walk quickly towards her.

Another page falls from the *Story of Us*, and I step carefully over it as I pass:

If I ever lose you it is because I can't see you.
And if ever I can't see you, it's only because you are inside me.

I watch her now, confident that I am unobserved. Her manner, like her posture, is cryptic and refutes easy comparisons. Her shoulders hunch, she stoops as she walks and there is an urgency about her gait that suggests guilty trespass or a person mapping an escape route. In effect, she seems in a rather desperate hurry to abandon my field of vision once and for all and to return to that vague, peripheral space at the limits of my perception, as though that were an arrangement we once found to be mutually advantageous or that she simply feels more at home there.

I call to her and I wave. 'Hey, Anne, wait up...'

She turns towards me and smiles, extending her hand towards mine. 'Hi, Marc,' she says with the sort of affection that teeters on the indulgent. 'I was just thinking about you.'

'Really?'

I catch her stealing the briefest glance at my birthmark, and I am grateful she decides not to remark upon it.

'Yes,' she adds in uncharacteristically hurried, nervous tones, 'I was just, you know, wondering how you were getting on with *Une Saison en Enfer*?'

My voice chooses this particular moment to loosen its tie and kick off its shoes. 'You know,' I say blandly. 'Slowly.'

She sighs. 'Come on, Marc, we need to talk.'

'Do we?'

She takes my arm suddenly and rather aggressively. 'Yes, we really do. There are lots of things that we need to discuss. Come...'

I find myself being marched away from La Place Ducale and up Avenue Charles Boutet once again, in the direction of the cemetery. For a moment, I consider telling her what I had just read about the exclamation marks, but there is something so purposeful about her general manner and demeanour at the moment that it dissuades me from embarking on the anecdotal or the trivial.

After walking for a minute or so, she stops at the junction with Rue Jean Bourguignon and points to a large open gate on the opposite side of the street. 'Come on,' she states, 'this is the place.'

Located unprepossessingly between a large and very suspiciously shuttered house and a pizza delivery shop, the double-fronted ironwork gate is mounted on two solid, unpretentious columns. Easy to overlook, I think, forgiving myself for having overlooked it in the past. At this distance, there is little to suggest what lies beyond the entrance. A modest municipal pet cemetery would have been my first guess.

Or somewhere Quakers go to sit quietly and regret being Quakers.

Anne takes my hand and leads me through the gate and down a narrow, grassy path until we find ourselves in a small, well-tended and well-curated public park. It's green and quiet and pretty.

'I have no money,' she says with the bland authority of information rather than confession, 'but if I did, I would bet you would not guess that somewhere like this even existed here in Charleville.'

I nod in agreement. 'It's very nice.'

She gestures vaguely towards a mature plum tree in a nearby border. 'It's beautiful here, huh? My friends and I come here often. It is always so peaceful. You are probably not aware of this, but Charleville is really very proud of its parks and its open green spaces. Actually, did you know that, in Charleville, there are seventy square metres of green space for every single inhabitant of the town?'

'No, I didn't know that.'

She smiles. 'There is still so much you don't know.' She clasps her thumb and her forefinger together exaggeratedly. 'You only see the tiny details. You have so little objectivity. You never notice the...' Her voice trails off as though she feels that this is not the best time to impart such information.

'So, what is this place?' I ask after almost a full minute's silence.

Anne takes a breath. 'Yes, I am glad you asked, Marc. This is called Parc Pierquin. It is named after Louis Pierquin. Not a name I imagine that you're familiar with, am I right?'

I shake my head.

'Then you will not know he was a teenage friend of Rimbaud's – although, to be fair, he is hardly a significant feature in the biographies.' She sneers theatrically at this fact for some reason. 'Yet the fact remains that, after Rimbaud's death, he acted as liaison between the publishers and the family members who actually owned the original poems. He wrote the first published obituary and he was also the person who informed Verlaine of the death of his former lover.'

'God, I didn't know any of that.'

'Of course you didn't. But Monsieur Pierquin has quite an important role in Rimbaud's story, does he not? Yet he somehow just doesn't add anything to the narrative, so pfft... we don't need him. And off he goes! Anyway, he loved Charleville and its history, and he built a house here, planted trees and was responsible for this beautiful garden. When he died, the whole place was opened to the public so people like you and me can come here now.'

She leans her head to one side and smiles at me. 'And of course, you should know by now that everything that happens in this town is nothing but a golden chain that somehow connects you back to Rimbaud.'

I smile back, but I say nothing. Instead, I look around the park and at the blue shadows cast by the conifers, and I find myself overwhelmed by the sudden curious idea that this is a place I have been visiting in dreams for as long as I can remember.

I feel a sudden breeze agitating the hairs on the back of my neck, and then Anne is standing in front of me. She is holding both of my hands in hers. She doesn't speak, but she leans towards me and kisses me. Once the initial surprise has passed, I find myself yielding and reciprocating. I open my eyes just long enough to see that hers are closed.

I surrender myself completely to the moment.

She pulls away fractionally at one point and, shaking her head, she presses her forefinger against my lips. 'No,' she whispers, 'say nothing.'

Then she kisses me again.

I can no longer think in physical or literal terms, only in simile and metaphor: what it reminds me of, what it makes me think of – abstractions, ideas. Words are useless! Words only mean other words! What is the point of that? It's no more than a bad joke rebranded as some Dadaist absurdity – like the machine whose sole function is to be a machine. This is the vanity and folly of human communication, and it is here where the entire flawed system fails. Right now, right here with Anne. I find myself at one of those impossibly rare moments – at the point where language fails and for which there can never be words or effective units of comparison.

I lose myself in Anne, in her taste and her smell, the warmth of her mouth, and the feel of her hair upon my cheek. For a moment, I become Anne, I have always been Anne, I feel myself to be a product of Anne…

And then she pulls away.

It is like the band in between tracks on a vinyl LP. You might like to think it's the conclusion to one song or the anticipation of the next.

But it is neither.

It is simply absolute silence.

Absence.

She retains her grasp of my hands and smiles at me. 'It's funny, you know, but you kiss exactly the same way I kiss.' She runs her fingertip along the arc of her top lip. 'I never felt that before. It's very nice,' she adds bashfully.

I can think of little to say in response to this, so instead, I ask simply, 'Is this why we came here?'

She looks shy and smiles defensively. 'Maybe, I just wanted to kiss you in a place that you would always remember. Somewhere you were visiting for the very first time.'

I cast my eyes downwards for fear of betraying myself too obviously. 'Thank you,' I whisper, barely above a mumble.

For when I lose you again, there is now somewhere in the world where I will be able to find you.

'Pardon?'

'Nothing...'

She looks at me sympathetically and then tilts her head to kiss me again.

'...*on se sent aux lèvres un baiser*

'*Qui palpite là, comme une petite bête...*'[35]

No, I think, not now; not any more. These are nothing more than words scribbled absently on a page. There is no sound, no voice, no vital living, breathing force, just the shadows cast by experience, rather than the experience itself. Traces. Meaningless traces. I feel only her mouth pressing against mine as a single warm tear falls on the open page in the *Story of Us*:

And on that far off day when my last breath leaves my body,
I pray I might be granted the strength
just to whisper her name a single, solitary, final time.
So it will be both the last thing I say
and the last thing I hear...

---

35 You feel on your lips a kiss. Which quivers there like a tiny animal...

19. Relief

When I next gaze upon her face, I am momentarily disturbed to see an expression of vague consternation. Her eyes widen and, abruptly, she pulls away from me.

'Oh, Marc, I'm sorry,' she says as I begin to feel an ancient childhood sense of vague panic rising in my chest.

'What is it?'

'I am so sorry; I really am, but right now I desperately need to have a pee.'

With some urgency, she departs our embrace, and I exhale loudly and possibly a little theatrically. I watch her vanish from view behind a hedge. 'I'm here,' she calls out cheerfully after a few moments, as though to reassure me that she hasn't been mugged or beaten.

'OK,' I say blandly.

I can see her feet under the hedge now. I look at them for a moment, but this, to me, suggests a level of intimacy that we have yet to establish, and so I turn away.

'*Je pisse vers les cieux bruns, très haut et très loin.*'[36]

---

36   I piss towards the brown skies, very high and very far.

I turn towards the voice. 'Can we do this some other time? I'm a bit, you know, busy at the moment.'

'*Ta tête se détourne: le nouvel amour! Ta tête se retourne — le nouvel amour!*'[37]

'You heard what he said. Run along now, there's a good chap. I'm sure you'll both have lots to talk about later.'

'*La Bouche d'Ombre...*'

'Go on... off you go. Hello, darling.'

'Hello, Mum. Well, what a complete and total surprise...'

'Oh, don't be like that. Where are your manners today?'

I shake my head. 'Well, you always were so good at picking your moments, weren't you?'

'Now that's a little unfair, I think. In fact, I would have thought this brief respite whilst your young lady friend is off *relieving* herself' – she invests the word with her traditional weary disapproval – 'is a perfect opportunity for us to catch up.'

'Oh God, please don't...'

'Oh, darling, don't be silly. In fact, I've always been incredibly envious of those who can attend to their bodily functions with such *equanimity*. I'm far too inhibited...'

I gaze upwards and focus my attention on the late-morning sun's gentle negotiations with the tops of the conifers. 'I don't really need that information right now, Mum, and I'm not sure if it's a conversation I would ever like to—'

She interrupts me. 'I was wrong, wasn't I?' she announces in an uncharacteristic tone that might have passed for contemplative. 'I mean, about the girl.'

'What exactly about the girl?' I am aware that I sound defensive and indignant.

'Actually, on reflection, I think she does seem genuine enough. And... and regardless of anything, well, she clearly loves you too, doesn't she?'

---

37 Your head is turning away: the new love! Your head is turning back – the new love.

'Oh for fuck's sake, Mum. How on earth can you say something like that? I've only just met her, that was the first time we actually—'

'Don't be ridiculous. If it's not there in those first few minutes, in those first few seconds even, then it's not love and it never will be. She may not even know it herself yet, any more than you do, but it's obvious. It's in the way she looks at you. How she can't help but smile when she's listening to you. How she tries to impress you. How she tries to confuse you and unsettle you, but all she wants is nothing more than your full and complete attention. All the time. Without intention or planning or even awareness, the two of you are creating a small, exclusive environment for yourselves; your shared space in this vast, cold, indifferent universe. You will add to it every day, through every single common experience, every kiss, every joke, every shared subliminal courtesy – it will all be part of it. Together, you will build a huge, high wall around your space and you will guard it and protect it with your lives. Forever.' She pauses, and I hear her exhale through a sigh. 'When you are together, whether you are talking or walking or eating or sleeping, there is no separation or transition any more. It is all part of the same journey. These daily, small ceremonies of devotion. I remember when I first met your father—'

'No, Mum; no, we are absolutely and categorically not having this conversation. And I don't mean just now – I mean not ever!'

'Oh, do try not to be so cynical about everything, not now. I know this is the tone you wanted to adapt for your novel. Re-examining all your past conflicts and disappointments and that growing sense of feeling adrift from your own times as you reflect on what is one of the few constants in your life.'

I shake my head, but I can think of nothing to say in reply.

'But don't you see that all this now, right here, is your absolute counterpoint to all that? Something that opposes and challenges your whole spirit of *disjointedness*. Why are you so obviously blind to your own narrative?'

Her question catches me off guard. 'My narrative, in case you have forgotten, is about Rimbaud.'

'It is *also* about Rimbaud,' she sneers victoriously. 'But it is about *her* as well.' She waves her hand vaguely in Anne's general direction. 'This new friend of yours! The lady who's currently over there weeing in the bushes! And of course it's about you and that sensation that is overwhelming you right now, as you wait impatiently, even anxiously, for her to return. Yes, that feeling! The uncertainty, the mounting panic, the sudden need and the fear. Hold on to it, cherish it and never lose it. She has that power over you now, and she always will. But in life, it is the best we can ever hope for. Love is what ignites the stars, darling; it's what lights those brilliant, glowing bonfires in the wilderness of our terrible daily despair and our endless banality. It is the poetry of the moment, but oh God, what a moment! It is still the only respite from the hideous desolation of mortality. And I should know...'

'Mum? Mum?' But her voice is quiet now, and I sense her no more. The slightest of winds, a dark-green agitation, but the rest is silence.

The rest is absence.

Then I hear her gentle footsteps on the grass. 'Who was that?'

I turn to my right. 'What do you mean?'

Anne tilts her head to one side, looks into my eyes and pouts quizzically. 'Who were you talking to?'

I feel exposed again. 'Oh, I was just... talking to myself.'

'You were not perhaps on the phone to your... to your girlfriend or somebody?'

'Oh God, no; absolutely not.'

'Good.' She smiles and takes my hand again. 'I am sorry about that, but I so needed a pee. It was the coffee, I think. I feel so much better now. Come, let's find somewhere we can sit.'

If one could be permitted to possibly raise one small criticism of Parc Pierquin it would be only to mention its lack of benches. But we find one eventually and we sit down.

Anne pats my arm quite forcefully, as though suggesting she urgently requires my attention. 'There is one thing I have been meaning to ask you, Marc. It is about Rimbaud. Did you not once write in a book that Rimbaud, or rather Poet Rimbaud from approximately 1871 to 1873, was actually a creation or a hoax perpetrated by Verlaine? Like it was some mad conspiracy theory you were having, and all Rimbaud's most notable works were in fact written by Verlaine.'

I'm not actually sure at this point if I am being mocked or not, but Anne seems to be enjoying herself.

'Yes, you wrote that there were historically three Rimbauds – the Charleville Rimbaud, the Paris Rimbaud and the Africa Rimbaud – and you were only interested in the Paris Rimbaud. You called him the Verlaine Rimbaud, as I recall. Anyway, I think you said that, in the photographs taken of Verlaine and Rimbaud at the time, their eyes are virtually identical and they are wearing the same clothes. So you then further speculate that the famous photograph we have of Rimbaud is basically that of Verlaine with a little theatrical make-up and a wig! There were other things as well, but I do not recall them so well.'

I consider it a small but noteworthy achievement that, for possibly the first and only time in my life, I manage at this point to simultaneously smile and frown. 'How do you know even about stuff like that? It was at least ten years ago.'

She smiles and runs her hand down the side of my thigh. 'You know me, Marc. I read a lot, and it was an interesting theory, I thought. You seemed to suggest that, ironically, Rimbaud was, in effect, Verlaine's *autre*. Of course, the whole thing was a little far-fetched, obviously.'

I put my hand on hers. 'I don't think it was a theory as such, I think it was just a device by which a character could demonstrate his own strange preoccupations. I'd intended his ideas to be provocative rather than definitive in any way.'

Awkwardly now, I recall the passages to which she is referring:

Let's remind ourselves of certain truths. That Rimbaud's greatest work, the work upon which his reputation is built, was written during his relationship with Verlaine, at a time when they actually lived together for long periods. That Verlaine wrote virtually no poetry for the first year they were together. That when he did start writing, he did so in a style that showed a remarkable similarity to Rimbaud's at the time. That the majority of Rimbaud's original manuscripts from this period are in Verlaine's handwriting. That Rimbaud would allegedly dictate his poems to Verlaine. That as they are parting after their final acrimonious meeting (which, according to some sources, has Rimbaud beating Verlaine unconscious and abandoning him at the roadside), Rimbaud simply hands over to Verlaine a pile of papers. These papers contain arguably the greatest sequence of poems ever written in the French language, namely Les Illuminations. *So, they argue, they fight and then – as they are separating, never to see each other ever again – Rimbaud just hands over the only copy of his finest work! Just ask yourself for a moment, how likely, how plausible is such a scenario? Yet these facts can be checked in any account of the lives of the poets. Furthermore, there is no doubt whatsoever that Rimbaud wrote no further poems of any consequence after this fateful meeting.*

There are a vast number of clues dotted around the place that confirm this hypothesis. Fellow poet Léon Valade, who may have been taken into Verlaine's confidence or heard a rumour, wrote in a letter in 1871 of a meeting with Verlaine during which he is introduced to Rimbaud. He refers to the young poet as being 'sous les auspices de Verlaine, son inventeur'. There is no alternative translation other than 'under the auspices of Verlaine, his inventor'. Inventor indeed? A curious word choice when one might expect to read 'friend', 'acquaintance', even 'partner' perhaps or possibly 'mentor'. Interestingly, both Monsieur Valade and the recipient of the letter, Émile Blémont, both feature in Fantin-Latour's legendary group portrait Le Coin de Table *alongside Verlaine and Rimbaud. As a matter of interest, I do believe there are certain sexual ambiguities in the representations of Rimbaud and Verlaine in that particular painting. For example, studied closely and in isolation, one might easily conclude that Verlaine resembles uncannily a woman disguised as a man, whilst Rimbaud looks like a man disguised as a woman.*

Another trick, another deception?

'There you go, Mum. It's all gone back to Rimbaud again now, you see?'

'Pardon?'

'Oh, I'm sorry,' I say clumsily. 'I'm just thinking out loud again.'

Anne smiles at me tolerantly. 'So, Marc, tell me, did you believe it, this whole crazy idea you had?'

I shake my head. 'Of course not, but I would've liked to think such a theory was credible or believable, if only for the sake of the story. I hoped it was probably enough that the character actually considered such an idea to be possible. But no, that's a long, long way from saying that I actually believed it.'

'So how did you, or your character, explain all the pictures and drawings of them together? As two different people.'

'Drawings are hardly irrefutable proof of anything.'

'True, I suppose. But do not forget that Verlaine went to prison for two years for shooting Rimbaud.'

'That's missing the point anyway; the issue was only about authorship and not actual existence!'

'Pfft...' She shrugs and exhales dramatically, suggesting that the subject is of no interest or consequence to her any more. Instead, she leans her head on my shoulder and strokes my cheek with her fingertips.

'I think I'm just going to have to kiss you again now. To stop you having any more of your mad ideas...'

20. Etoile

A number of critics have pointed out how frequently the word *'saisons'* occurs in Rimbaud's writing. Some have even suggested it is as though he finds the traditional, empirical method of measuring time restrictive in some way, and instead, he relies upon an alternative of his own invention – a season. A unit of time that might be personal, instinctive or even emotional. This relationship is a season, the time I lived in that house is a season and, indeed, my childhood is a season.

We grant Rimbaud these extraordinary freedoms, these deliberate and outrageous disconnections from convention, and then we envy him. I suppose it could be argued that we invest him with these precise freedoms solely that we might envy him.

Personally, I have a 'Rimbaud season', and I have been having approximately the same one for something like forty years. It usually starts around the beginning of April and, generally, runs well into June. There are exceptions: the extension in this current year being a case in point. But regardless of most social or emotional or even financial factors, it is during that time, as the weather starts getting warmer, I will always turn to Rimbaud.

Perhaps I can conceive of flight and escape better when the days grow longer.

During that couple of months, I also listen to music that connects me straight back to my late teens: Patti Smith, The Ramones, The Clash, etc. It all seems to be part of the same process of rejuvenation. But there is Rimbaud, who is, for me, the focus for all that has not yet been denied me.

Over the years, my identification with Rimbaud has undergone a subtle but by no means undramatic shift. For so many years, I saw myself as trailing in the wake of the *rebel poet*, the eternal outsider, the idealist, the non-conformist, and the man who could articulate his dreams – and therefore my own – better than any man. And if not exactly redemption, I could find something like justification encrypted in those relatively few poems, which I read over and over again.

Then at some point that I would estimate to be between thirty-five and forty-five, this underwent a radical change. The passionate projection of myself onto my personal hero remained entirely constant, yet it seemed to me to be for completely different reasons. With the passing of youth, there went in tandem – reluctantly and sadly – the passing of all that brash, swaggering youthful self-belief. Instead, I found myself identifying – literally, to the point of envy – with the idea of a man abandoning his own history, even his own extraordinary gifts, to embark on an entirely new adventure, knowing that the consequences of such escape and exile are that he can never return or even look back.

Indeed, as I grew older, there were many things in my life I would be happy never to return to. And I too longed for a new identity and the freedom that this would confer upon me. I could then, like Rimbaud, wander the surface of the earth like the great eternal pagan and nomad, traffic in the unseen and the unknown, and in time, lose all sense of the past.

And all sense of myself.

So my Rimbaud season has remained constant, and now, after forty years, it has led me to Anne, so at least I can feel a degree of vindication in that respect.

One afternoon, I lay on my bed listening to the rain.
Then I caught sight of your face,
And suddenly my ears could hear rain no more.
They could only hear the music.

There are times when the absurdity and vanity of defining myself as a writer, in even the vaguest capacity, abandons me totally.

I really have no words for this any more.

There is no language available to me, and no apposite simile or metaphor. No deceptively simple literary device that I can draw upon that might render the experience more accessible.

Nothing.

At a stretch, I might be able to envisage my current state of mind as a mathematical equation. I certainly seem to be at the point where virtually all linguistic techniques begin to falter and fail dismally to convey the enormity of this experience.

But then, as a third alternative, I picture an incredibly detailed and complex astronomical model, one that maps the heavens in three dimensions. I see the vast numbers of stars in the limitless darkness, but some shine brighter than others. These I claim on my behalf as representative of the rare, fleeting moments of pure, unaccountable joy I have found in my life – those very moments that made me who I am. Moments that live independently of context or memory, but that remain pivotal. Hearing Charlie Parker for the first time, walking in Congo Square in New Orleans, seeing Guernica in Madrid, kissing Anne in Parc Pierquin and all the others that hang so brightly in the awful, unremitting blackness.

These are my stars.

My givens.

My certainties.

They exist randomly and independently, with no sense of correlation or any tangible relationship between them until that one tiny sliver of time, less than a nanosecond in reality, when you find yourself at that one solitary, unique and absolutely precise point in the whole story of all your days. It is a once-in-a-lifetime occurrence, and if you were to glance over your shoulder at that exact fraction of a second, you would see – just for a fleeting instant – all your stars lining up along some perfect celestial arc that is sublime and breathtaking in its utter beauty.

A glimmering golden chain unites and links them all together; one end is at the beginning of all things, visible and invisible, whilst you hold the other tightly in your hand. At that moment, and only at that moment, your life is the closest it will ever come to the idea of infinity; all doors and all limitless possibilities are open, and the unknown is finally available and made manifest to you.

Imagine, then, that on the same heavenly chart there is an alternative arc: the linear representation of another life, another set of stars. Imagine that, at the precisely the same moment of awareness, the arcs of these two lives actually touch and fuse together.

It is not love.

It is beyond love.

It is an event of truly cosmic proportions.

'Oh, and just look how we are dancing now…'

21. ROSE

'Come on, Marc, we go now,' she says, effectively curtailing my train of thought. She grips my hand with a surprising strength that I flatter myself is born out of some sort of conviction or sudden sense of attachment. 'There is something I need to do now. Somewhere I need to go.'

'Where do you need to go?'

'No, I can't tell you that, but you have to meet me back here in an hour.' She smiles playfully, her face as animated as mine feels paralysed, and I wonder, given our current situation, how soon I will be able to kiss her again.

'An hour?' I ask.

'Yes, an hour.'

'OK,' I say, attempting to mask a feeling of vague disappointment.

'Just one thing,' she adds with a shrug as she pushes the tip of her tongue ambiguously out of the corner of her mouth.

'Anything,' I reply with possibly more extravagance than her request warrants.

'Will you give me twenty euros, please?'

'Twenty euros?'

She nods. 'Yes, twenty euros.'

I reach into my pocket. 'Of course. But why do you want twenty euros, Anne?'

She turns away. 'I cannot tell you, Marc. It is a secret, but soon you will know.'

'Well, may I come with you?' My voice, I am aware, is teetering on pleading.

She looks at me with determination, but not entirely without sympathy. She strokes my arm. 'No, Marc, you must just be back here in an hour. You will see. I promise.'

I watch her walking now in the opposite direction back down Avenue Charles Boutet towards Place Ducale, and I want to follow her and I want to call after her – I do not want to lose sight of her. But I fight these urges. I imagine her expression as she turns around to discover me a few metres behind her.

She would know then.

She would know everything.

She walks in a hurried, purposeful manner, with an almost cartoon-like gait, from which I manage to quickly infer an undercurrent of subterfuge. I feel utterly alone, and it might be envy or resentment, but it saddens me deeply to think she is not feeling the same as me at this moment.

Every line, every staggeringly poor, clichéd line I have ever written, every worthless phrase so lacking in insight or wit was on some level, I suddenly realise, an attempt to articulate the wretchedness of loneliness. To express, in effect, what I am feeling right now at this exact instant. In my defence, I should state that such a skill is an elusive one – loneliness is that lingering trace of an ancient presence in the universe of cold and terrible absence.

So, to summarise, I feel that I am once again the *Most Conspicuously Lonely Figure in Any Given Landscape*, the eternal tragic-comic figure of my own creation, walking the margins of my own life and off the pages of the books I will never have the skill, the temerity or the fire within me to write.

And if only in death
We live together.
Then take my hand
And hasten us towards
The darkness that is our star.

'Oh man, that's heavy...'

I feel a firm hand on my shoulder.

'I mean, it's beautiful an' all, but whoa, maybe youse need just a little light and shade dere.'

I sigh. 'Maybe...'

'I mean, *my blues is just a blue light a shinin' in my eyes;* 's'all the same shit, baby, when you'se get down to it.'

I turn towards him and smile. 'Hey, Mister Johnson.'

'Hey, boy. Seems y'all maybe feelin' a little lonesome right about now?'

I point, with unconvincing disinterest, at Anne in the distance. 'There she goes,' I say in a colourless voice. 'I am supposed to meet her in an hour. That's what she said anyway,' I add in hurried, vague tones, suddenly aware that I am making a face that is an approximation of the very expression she so frequently effects to indicate disinterest.

The great Delta bluesman chooses this moment to take his hand away from my shoulder. 'So, what's da problem, then? Can't say I follow you.'

I shake my head. 'I don't really know. I just think she's gone to meet someone, and I doubt... well, somehow I don't think she'll be back.'

'Meet someone? Y'all mean she be meetin' herself a man?'

'No, well, I don't know... maybe?'

Robert replies with a low, rattling chuckle. 'Whoa, man. I kinda think you's bein' a bit harsh there on the lady.'

'You do?'

'Yeah, man. Ladies have dose lady things dey have to do

167

sometimes. Kinda vexes me too, but feelin' a little lonesome can be good for you sometimes. It sharpens the mind too, boy. I mean, what else is a man gonna write about, you know?'

I turn towards him and, genuinely, I have never seen so much wisdom in one man's eyes. 'Maybe that works for you...'

'Works for all of us. We're all in da same story somewhere, in da same song even, but we're just at different ways along. Maybe you feel you's near the beginning or the end, but it's always the same whatever you do. Ain't no escape from not one tiny bit of it.'

I smile at him. 'Yeah, for sure...'

'So what else do youse think art is for?'

'I don't know. Cages for the vagaries of the human heart?'

He chuckles again. 'Yeah, somethin' like dat! Hey, boy do you remember dis one?'

He takes his wood-bodied National off his shoulder and plays a variant on the introduction to the second recorded take of 'Love In Vain Blues'. The tempo is a little slower, which gives the phrase greater resonance. He smiles at me warmly and then, skipping the traditional first verse, he opens by singing what I recall to be the second:

I love my baby and I can't stand to leave her be
I love my baby and I can't stand to leave her be
But her no good ways done always bring me to my knees.

The music begins to fade, but I have always loved this particular song.

And I even know the day I first heard it.

It was Christmas Day, 1975.

I can say that with absolute authority. I was fifteen, and I'd asked for and been given a copy of the aforementioned *King Of The Delta Blues Singers* LP as my Christmas present that year. God, I remember it so clearly. I remember struggling with the music: it sounded so alien to me, it was music of a different time, the sound was primitive, and the lyrics were hard to decipher, but I had to keep listening to it. It was important; I understood that much even at fifteen, as I attempted to make sense of a man articulating the existential despair of the human condition in a I-IV-V musical format. And furthermore, to me in 1975, this wasn't just a record or a present, this was *An Event* and this LP that I held in my trembling hands would be part of how I defined myself in the future! In some ways, that thrill has never left me, and every time I hear Robert Johnson, part of that morning ignites in me again. Of course, nowadays, all that music is available and accessible to everyone all the time. I don't consider this to be a positive or negative thing, and in truth, I don't think I actually care very much.

'Besides, you remember what it was like being a kid back then?'

But there is no one there.

Once again alone but for my own uncertainties, I wander away from the park with no particular destination in mind. I walk down some of the adjacent streets on Avenue Charles Boutet, occupying myself as best I can. My mind plays out scenarios during which I wait until nightfall for Anne to come back, scared to leave the park in case I miss her. But she never returns, and I never see her again. Eventually, I make my way back to the Hôtel Couleurs Sud and begin to write. I write frantically all night, I don't sleep, and by morning, I have written the first 10,000 words of the *Story of Us*. The book that will occupy me, on and off, for the rest of my life, as I attempt to capture the essence of my feelings for Anne after knowing her for only a few brief, flickering moments.

'*J'ai compris qu'elle était à sa vie de tous les jours; et que le tour de bonté serait plus long à se reproduire qu'une étoile.*'[38]

---

38 I understood that she has gone back to her daily life; and this kind turn and the possibility of its recurrence was now more distant than a star.

I hear the voice, but my shoulders are tense, and I do not wish to turn around and face him.

'*Elle n'est pas revenue, et ne reviendra jamais.*'[39]

Not now.

Instead, I lean forwards and walk quickly back to Parc Pierquin.

To my surprise, to my delight and to my astonishment even, she is standing there, next to the gate where we parted earlier.

'There you are,' she says as I approach her. 'I thought you weren't coming.'

I can think of nothing to say, so partly out of unspoken gratitude, I simply kiss her on the cheek. The formality of the gesture immediately strikes us both as slightly inappropriate given our most recent encounter.

'Look,' she adds, in an attempt to offset any lingering awkwardness, as she holds up a carrier bag for my inspection.

I don't know what I was imagining I would see inside it, but a gardening trowel and a rose bush would have been pretty far down my list. 'Right,' I say blandly, wondering if this was the best possible use of my twenty euros.

'You like?'

'Of course. Yes, it's very nice.'

She points lazily, limply and with more enthusiasm than geographic accuracy. 'I went to that place up the road behind the station, to the little garden centre over there.'

'I see.'

'Come on. Whilst there's nobody about...'

She takes my hand, and we creep back into the park like the shameful and notorious rogues we are. We retrace our steps until we are standing roughly at the point where we'd kissed an hour or so previously. We look at each other for a moment, and I detect in her expression a solemnity I have hitherto not witnessed.

---

39 She didn't return and never will return.

'There,' she says, abruptly, pointing towards the nearby border. 'I think that would be the closest point.'

She chooses this moment to remove the trowel and the rose bush from the carrier bag and, smiling, she holds them up for me to see. I nod and smile back.

'See that?' She points to the label on the packaging around the base of the stem, which features an image of the rose in full bloom and the words '*Arthur Rimbaud*'. 'Yes, perhaps you did not know, but they named a rose after him.'

I shake my head. 'No, I didn't know that.'

'It is for us. It is why I went to the shop to buy it. I thought you'd be so pleased! Oh come on, Marc...'

I still feel that I am the inductee at the ceremony, the unenlightened, the uninitiated, the irredeemably and eternally clueless...

I frown. 'Where...? I mean... what exactly...?'

'We are going to plant a rose bush, right here in the park! Our rose bush, the Arthur Rimbaud rose bush,' she explains, a little tersely, as though such an activity was the most obvious and self-evident one that she could possibly conceive.

'We are?'

'Yes, we are going to plant it just here.' She points. 'Right next to where we kissed – for the first time.' She turns towards me and kisses me on the mouth. 'So, it will always be here, and whatever happens in the future, whether it's you and me together or just one of us on our own, we can come here and see our rose, and our moment that we shared here today will never be forgotten. This will always be here to remind us.'

She is smiling at me now. 'And even in lives as wretched and as damned as ours, Marc, there is always the possibility of roses.'

'I don't know what to say...'

'So say nothing; just pass me the trowel when I ask for it.'

I follow close behind her and now, in my head, the unuttered words come quickly again.

Tumbling and falling, I chase them and catch them:

For in truth I would rather die alongside you
Than live my life apart from you.

22. Mongrels

For I saw in you the mongrel angel
That saw in me the same.

So where is Rimbaud now?
   If not in this youthful folly of mine?
   In this wonderful absurdity?
   And us Mongrel Angels?
   Or have I followed Rimbaud and come here simply to reinvent the idea of love in my own mind?
   To dislocate it from any previous notion or definition?
   And thus I was never made sad, bitter or angry, or was consumed with failure, resentment or recrimination, because on all previous occasions, my feelings were illusory in the first instance.

For I loved in you the mongrel angel
That loved in me the same.

   'Marc!' she calls, and I turn back to face her. 'Look!'

She indicates the stem of the Arthur Rimbaud rose, which she has now planted, coincidentally or otherwise, adjacent to the bush behind which she'd peed earlier. 'The man at the shop, he says it will be in full bloom next spring.' She looks, I think, genuinely proud of her effort and possibly the original inspiration behind it.

'*En somme, une Fleur, Romarin*
'*Ou Lys, vive ou morte, vaut-elle*
'*Un excrément d'oiseau marin?*'[40]

I think I have actually been expecting this particular interjection for a while now, and so ignoring it is a far from difficult task. Instead, I look straight at Anne.

She smiles and opens her palm, so I see the traces of soil on her hand. I see her face glowing and joyous in the direct sunlight and the shadow she casts on the mellow, ancient brick wall behind her, and I feel this sudden surge of comfort.

I feel weightless and alive.

I think it is because she reminds of a picture in an old illustrated edition of *The Secret Garden* I once had as a child.

But this is not right.

Alternatively, the full colour picture on the right-hand page of a much loved and battered old Ladybird book: *Helping in the Garden. What To Look for in Summer* – quite possibly the most perfect book title of all time.

No, not that.

Or it is an image I recall as a framed print on the wall of my grandparents' house?

Wrong again.

Then surely it's a still frame from an old BBC adaptation of some classic rural novel, maybe something from Hardy or George Eliot?

But no, none of these are right either.

---

40 In short, is a flower, rosemary or lilly, alive or dead, worth any more than seagull shit?

Somehow, I cannot shake myself free of the idea that I have witnessed this exact scene before me a dozen times, 1,000 times, maybe on literally infinite occasions. All that is logical contradicts this, but it presents itself in my mind as a knowledge as certain as memory. We have done this before on an uncountable number of times, and I know this to be an empirical fact. Maybe you'd need Aristotle's intellect or Yeats' genius to make that great leap into brilliant speculation and articulate this exact sensation. It is a sudden rush of certainty that Anne and I have this connection that neither begins nor ends and that it transcends any notion of linear time.

'So, what do you think?' she asks coyly.

'It's just beautiful,' I say as I gently and instinctively press my index finger to the corner of my eye.

She notices this and its small implication immediately. 'Oh, Marc,' she utters, and she hurries towards me. She kisses me on my cheekbone and smiles at me. Then she says slowly and emphatically, 'I am going to kiss away every tear you have ever cried. Would that be OK?'

I manage to nod an affirmation.

'Good. You can do the same for me too, if you like.'

I nod again.

The voice chooses this moment to return once again. I hear it behind me, heavy with sarcasm, but again, I don't turn around. Neither do I respond in any way.

'*C'est l'aimée ni tourmentante ni tourmentée.*

'*L'aimée.*'[41]

To be entirely honest, there is nothing in my life that has prepared me for Anne. I have no experience upon which I can draw. Anne is different. Different, I suspect, from anyone I will ever meet. I have known her for just a single day, yet I am already secretly jealous, suspicious and hateful of every second of her life that she has spent away from me.

---

41   It is the beloved neither tormenting nor tormented.
The beloved.

175

I've had girlfriends, partners, lovers, fuck buddies and those who would refuse to self-identify as anything more meaningful than acquaintances. I even once had a wife! But they all eventually culminated in final acts that were depressingly similar. So, invariably, I felt it was my fault or we had just fallen victim to some previously undisclosed failing of mine. But I can't relate a single one of my experiences in the past to my feelings for Anne – at this distance, they feel to me like the emotional and psychological equivalent of cycling on the pavement.

It's true that I do believe it's ultimately the curse of all couples that they eventually turn into their own tribute act. Endlessly referencing, rehashing or attempting to revive those fleeting, ancient seconds of shared wonder, perfection and significance. An attempt to connect with something that was once infinitely simpler, easier and purer. I would even accept that it is this carefully curated self-mythologising that remains the key to a long and healthy relationship! The past is safe; it doesn't alarm us, worry us, or make us feel confused or disconnected. We have already risen to its challenges and problems. And look, we're still here! The future is something to fear, so why not take comfort in all our lovely, old value systems and seek the sanctuary of what is defined and certain in our wonderful simpleton minds?

Nostalgia is therefore a form of cowardice.

But in a broader sense and like no other generation before us, we live in the era of tribute acts – this over-reverence for what we once loved and for what we fear is now slipping away from us. And it could effectively be argued that Brexit stoked the imaginations of my fellow countrymen and became in a very real sense the greatest tribute act of all. Ladies and gentlemen, please put your hands together now for the Bootleg Britain...

'Hey, Marc, what are you laughing at?'

I blink. 'Sorry. Was I laughing?'

'Just a little bit,' says Anne with a vague shrug. 'Come on, I have to take your picture. I take it on your phone. My phone is rubbish. Come and stand here by the stem of our rose bush...'

I have no wish to correct her, of course, but it is not technically a bush at the moment – just bare twigs and branches. However, it has a satisfying asymmetrical shape, I think, and I wonder if I were to trace a pattern of its very extremities, I could find the five points of a star.

'Here you go...' I hand her my phone as I step, with possibly unnecessary caution, off the grass and onto the border. I don't really know what a suitable expression would be under the circumstances, so I try to keep my face as neutral as possible as she takes my picture. Have we done this before? Have we commemorated the moment in some way? I'm sure we have; I know we have.

I take her picture. I take a couple, in fact. She smiles, and I think I almost envy the way she seems to inhabit her own life completely. By comparison, I feel like the cautious guest, hovering in the hallway and permanently wiping my feet on the doormat of my own existence.

Presently, she takes my arm, and we walk away from our rose. We walk in silence, but after covering a distance of about ten metres and as if responding to some unheard inner command, we both stop walking at precisely the same instant and turn back towards the border. It is as though neither of us is quite brave enough to abandon this perfect moment of ours.

We say nothing, only because there are times when nothing needs to be said.

When we finally leave the park, she starts to talk about Rimbaud again and returns to the particular subject she had touched on over breakfast earlier.

'You know, maybe it is not good to be judgemental either, particularly when you recall that Verlaine was ten years Rimbaud's senior and Rimbaud was only sixteen. But even though the very first letter Rimbaud sent Verlaine has not survived, there is a record of the poems he included with the correspondence. One of them, Les Effarés features the rhymes *culotte* and *tremblotte*. The identical two rhymes feature in an earlier poem of Verlaine's, En Bateau, with which Rimbaud would have certainly been familiar. It seems likely this was a deliberate and perhaps subtle attempt to flatter the older man and to play on his vanity. I just cannot believe this was in any way coincidental or inadvertent. Rimbaud was an incredibly smart and devious adolescent, and I'm certain he knew exactly what he was doing. To him – initially, at least – I think it was simply a smart career move.'

'I'm sure that's possible,' I say in the muted tones of a man whose mind is elsewhere. 'It sounds very plausible.'

'I think we should always be very careful when we make assumptions regarding who, exactly, is preying on whom. Do you not think so, Marc?'

'Yes, I mean, obviously…'

'Sometimes, it is hard to know precisely who is the seducer and who is the seduced?' She looks at me, frowns for a moment, and then quickly breaks into probably the broadest and most joyful smile I have ever seen.

Faintly now, I see the outline of our rose bush on the front cover of the *Story of Us*. Unexpectedly, as I contemplate the image, it changes, and now I'm looking at the buds in full bloom as the words of the title rearrange themselves.

They now read: *What To Look for in Summer.*

23. Fables

'So, Marc, are you telling me you've never felt like planting a rose just like that?'

Anne and I are now sitting outside the café on La Place Ducale where I'd had my lunch the previous day. 'I mean, you must have had loads of girlfriends in your time – did you never think about doing something like that?'

'Loads?' I say, uncertain if I should take pride or umbrage at the suggestion, whilst seeming to avoid the main point of her question.

'Lots then!'

'Actually,' I concede, attempting a self-effacing shrug, 'probably not as many as you think.' I huff distractedly – it is a ludicrous and ridiculous assertion considering I have absolutely no idea of the actual number she might have in mind.

She laughs at this. 'Ah, well, you see, they probably all left you because you weren't romantic enough!'

I gaze over the rooftops on the opposite side of the square. 'It's possible, I suppose, but usually, it was just all that other stuff. You know, the usual nonsense. General bad timing, specific incompatibility, lack of commitment, too much commitment, political and religious differences, and, oh… on one very famous occasion, bad handwriting.'

Anne pouts. 'Bad handwriting?'

'Yes, a girl I knew back in the early 1990s; she was really nice too. We went out a couple of times; she lived over in Tooting, Wandsworth, somewhere over there. Anyway, to cut a long story short, I spent the night with her once at her flat. It was a great night too. We got on really well, had a takeaway, watched a movie, laughed a lot and actually had sex for the first time, which was good in that kind of cautious, careful, unspectacular preliminary way. It was a Friday night, and I had to leave early in the morning; as she wanted a lie-in, I told her I would be really quiet and not disturb her. So far so good?'

'Yes, please carry on.'

'So, as I'm getting ready to leave, given that we'd spent the night together, I just didn't feel comfortable going without saying goodbye. So I scribble her a little note and leave it propped up against the kettle. Just a couple of lines – nothing much more than pleasantries, really. But it might have been a bit dark in the kitchen or maybe I was in too much of a hurry, but it seems the loop of my d appeared to be separated from its stem. I thought I'd written:

'Hope to see you soon, Love and stuff ! xx'

'But she read my chatty "love and stuff" as "love *anal* stuff", and consequently, never spoke to me ever again! My cheerful sign-off was transformed into this terrible, presumptuous sexual request! A demand, even! Seriously, I found all this out a few days later through a mutual acquaintance. I tried calling her to explain, but she refused to answer her phone.'

Anne covers her face and laughs into her hands. 'Oh, Marc… is that true?'

'Absolutely! Every single word! And why oh why did I have to put in that fucking exclamation mark? You know, I always thought that might have been the last detail that irredeemably sealed my fate. But I promise you, I was a lot more careful with my penmanship and particularly the loops of my d's after that experience. But to this day, I'm pretty sure there are pubs in Tooting Bec that I should probably best avoid.'

She appears evidently amused by my story, and her laughter seems genuine enough. 'Poor you,' she says eventually. She lowers her head and reaches her hand across the table towards mine.

She fixes her stare upon me and smiles. 'Marc,' she adds suddenly and rather abruptly, as if summoning me from a distance, 'do you love me?'

I feel my chest vibrate as I inhale. I hold my breath. I prepare to speak.

But before I can reply, she continues, 'That is what we are told Rimbaud was always asking Verlaine. Do you love me? But do you *love* me? Then he would ask him to prove it. There was a café in Montmartre they frequented called Le Rat Mort, and on one occasion, he demanded that Verlaine put his hand on their table in front of him. Rimbaud then stabbed him in the wrist. It was how he would seek evidence of his lover's devotion.'

'Maybe,' I suggest, 'they should have planted a rose.' I mean this quite genuinely, but I fear my tone might be teetering on facetious.

Anne pouts and seems to be trying to read my expression. 'Yes, quite…'

I smile defensively as she gathers her thoughts.

'Anyway,' she says with a shrug, 'most of those stories about Rimbaud at Le Rat Mort are just stupid fucking nonsense. The classic *naughty boy* stories. You Rimbaud fans repeat these fables with a sort of perverse pride. Look, I am wicked and daring and terrible simply by association. Like the time he allegedly made a painting out of his own shit, have you heard that one?'

'I don't think so.'

'It is a ridiculous fantasy. A legend, a joke! But it gets passed down by biographers and writers, year after year. Like the story about Charles Cros, do you know that one?'

I think for a moment. 'Rings a bell. Is it something about his drink?'

'Yes! Yes!' She looks delighted. 'According to so many of the main sources, one evening at Le Rat Mort, when Cros returned from the toilet, Rimbaud – who had apparently borrowed some sulphuric acid especially for the occasion – had poured the acid into Cros' drink!'

I recall the story, but I confess I have never paid it much attention.

Anne continues, her voice increasingly agitated, 'Why was this story ever repeated? This is just another ridiculous anecdote. I mean, was he actually intending to kill him? And how and from where do you actually *borrow* sulphuric acid? The whole story is like an ancient, bad black-and-white cartoon! In fact, that is exactly what it is! Critics dispute the dates of the poems in *Les Illuminations*, but no one ever questions these fucking idiotic stories? You see, Marc, as familiar as we may be with 'Le Bateau Ivre' or 'Voyelles', we are also equally familiar with those stupid legends, and it's hard to take the poet and the poetry out of all the mythology that has built up around him. You must not let yourself get dragged down by that.'

I look at her face and I lose myself. I lose all my normal reticence, my customary faux cynicism, and I seem to no longer be in possession of any of my usual defence mechanisms. 'Well, I was hoping,' I explain in a small, hesitant voice, which is no longer mine and no longer a voice over which I seem to have any control, 'that as soon as I get something down on paper, you could read it through, maybe? Let me know that I'm on the right track at least. Would that be OK?'

'Oh, Marc, that would be perfect. I would love to read it. I'm sure it will be brilliant.'

I look down and focus on her hand, which is still resting on mine. 'Oh, I don't know about that, but you know, you have to just… try, don't you?'

She grips my hand tightly. 'So, Marc,' she says softly, 'do you love me?'

I raise my eyes and look into the beautiful paradox of her face. At once, I feel simultaneously excited, calm, terrified and reassured.

It is the farthest point to which I will ever wish to travel, yet it is also my home.

Under my scrutiny, the face breaks into a slight smile. 'It is all right; I promise I'm not going to try to stab—'

'Of course I love you,' I declare, 'of course I do.'

That I alone had possessed this information for even the shortest fraction of time and not shared or even articulated it seems suddenly absurd, cruel, and the most bizarre and extreme kind of self-loathing I can imagine. The words enter our shared history at that moment, after which the idea of *us* will become a structure – tangible and defined. At the precise point where our two arcs overlap, a star now explodes into existence, after which there will be only a single arc.

I turn my head slightly and watch him as – with a languid, gentle grace – he now positions himself on the vacant chair to my immediate right. The benign and smiling slim Irishman, with the genial face, who was born a mere eleven years after Rimbaud, looks at me over his spectacles. 'Don't worry, he is mistaken,' he whispers, and I hear immediately the kindness in his voice. 'Perhaps it is just the natural cynicism and wariness of youth. But in truth, lovers reinvent love every single moment they are together – otherwise, they can have no possible reason to refer to their union as such.'

I look at Anne again, and she smiles at me, but it is a different smile – the very subtle change in emphasis only visible, I would like to believe, to me. I am hearing music again too, and for some reason, I find myself concentrating on that eight bar half-time B section in 'Milestones' by Miles Davis. It is louche and elegant; a stark contrast to the main A-section theme, which is dynamic and percussive. It is a bold and audacious departure. A huge risk. It is wrong, yet it is utterly right at the same time, and it is hard to conceive of anything else that would sound quite so exhilarating.

Now, in my head, it's Yeats playing against Rimbaud.

'Another thing,' he says as he taps my arm with some urgency. 'You mentioned earlier that if Adam the hermaphrodite was made in God's image then that would also make God a hermaphrodite. So, I was thinking then, if one adheres to the concept of the Holy Trinity, would that not make Jesus hermaphroditic also? You see, for many years I wondered why so many Renaissance painters followed the odd convention of portraying Jesus as a beautiful woman with a beard! So from that perspective, he has the recognisable traits of both sexes. That always used to fascinate me. I remember once, as a young man when I was—'

'Merde!'

I hear the word as a passer-by casts a brief shadow across Anne's face.

'Surely, you must have guessed,' I suggest, returning to our conversation after another moment or two of silence has passed between us. 'You had to have some inkling of how I felt.'

'No, well, I hoped, perhaps...'

Briefly, I turn to the gentleman once more and back again to Anne. 'I think, if I'm honest, and I can see no reason why I shouldn't be right now, I felt something the very first moment I saw you outside the Carrefour.'

She gently exhales my name: 'Marc...'

And I have never in my life heard my own name uttered so evocatively and so perfectly.

It is the comforting whisper in the terrible darkness of all my old dreams.

'Yes?'

'It's just...' she hesitates, 'well, I can't believe that someone like you could ever love... someone like me.'

I glance again to my side, return the gentleman's smile, take a breath and, one day, somewhere faraway, I sit down and I write this:

But that, I said,
Was one of the reasons why I love you so much.
Don't you see?
It's because someone like you
Thinks I'm someone like me...

24. Novel

'Well, he seemed very nice, I thought. Quite charming, in fact.'

'Who seemed nice?'

My mother, in her customary manner, chooses to completely ignore my question. 'I think I was imagining that he might have one of those lovely, soft Dublin accents. But he didn't really seem to have much of an accent at all, did he? It's a shame he had to go.'

I mumble something that might have been affirmative. Or it might not.

She continues. 'But actually, it might be good to have a voice other than Rimbaud's. Certainly, a more appropriate source of ideas for a more, shall we say, mature man. Referencing Rimbaud at every possible opportunity is, you must admit, rather like dragging your old train set around with you. Mr Yeats gives a sort of balance to things and highlights the shift in your thinking. Particularly now because of your feelings for Anne Autry.'

Anne had left our table a few moments ago to answer her phone, and I can see her a few metres away, nodding and laughing, and I wonder who she is talking to.

And I wonder if I should feel threatened.

'Dad never let me play with it.'

'Play with what?'

'My train set, so it's a poor analogy.'

'He had his reasons, I'm sure. He was probably just concerned for your safety. OK, an old toy then, like that stuffed, pink elephant I made for you when you were very young. It would be like carrying that around with you.'

'Again, that's a poor metaphor. I actually still have that elephant in my possession. I call him Clearly – because he's clearly an elephant. He's battered and faded and has been repaired a few times, but he's still going. He normally lives on my chest of drawers and guards my hats.'

My mother, who is now sitting opposite me in the chair where Anne had been sitting, smiles at me with all her usual maternal ambiguity. She promptly decides to return to the previous subject. 'Anyway, I am really glad she makes you so happy,' she says evenly, as though she's mindful not to stress any individual word.

'She does, Mum; she does.'

'You know, it's funny, darling, but I keep remembering a passage from that first novel you ever wrote. Do you remember any of that?'

I put my hand over my face. 'Oh God, no. It was terrible. I thought I'd destroyed all evidence of the damn thing. It was just embarrassing.'

'You were still in your twenties; you were comparatively young.' She smiles reflectively. 'You used to send me chapters to read. I saved them all.'

'Oh, Mum, why would you even do that?'

'But of course I did! Because you are my son and I was proud of you. I still am...'

'Don't! Just don't say, "in a funny way". Try to resist. Do your best. Please!'

'Oh dear. I must say, you're being particularly oversensitive today, darling.'

'Oversensitive? I still wake up screaming some nights whenever my subconscious fails to block the memory of that idiotic bloody thing and just one solitary line sneaks back into my mind!'

She smiles again, the authoritative smile of someone who is not about to be swayed by any alternative argument. 'Stylistically, perhaps, it was a little journalistic at times, with loads of typos, as I recall.'

'Yeah, but you were always the best proofreader I ever knew. Seriously, you had a real flair for it.'

'Thank you, darling. You're very kind. But I always thought your story had one or two very interesting ideas.'

Silently, I wince at her deliberate use of the word 'story', and then I exhale loudly and dismissively in the unmistakeable manner of Anne. 'Not as I recall.'

My mother then goes on to remind me that there was a passage at some point in the text where I referenced Plato and the idea of a hermaphroditic race being divided into incomplete male and female components and the consequential urge to locate the original divine other. She then delights in quoting a passage during which I wrote that the 'absurdity or complete futility of the quest being one of the first basic human dilemmas – the certain knowledge that, somewhere, there exists your absolute perfect opposite'. Apparently, I actually referred to such a union as 'an actual recapturing of that lost state of grace'.

Not being one to ever let such an opportunity pass her by, she concludes by reminding me that Plato clearly had the idea before Aristotle.

I shake my head nervously. 'Maybe, yes… But did I really write all that?'

'Yes, you did. It's evidently a concept you've been formulating for a number of years now.'

'Well, it's an interesting idea,' I say, uncertain whether I feel embarrassed or a little annoyed at myself for not having remembered the earlier reference.

'Do you believe it?' she asks matter-of-factly. 'Any of it? I mean, as an actual reality?'

I sense the direction her line of questioning is heading in, and it is not a subject with which I feel comfortable at the moment.

Perhaps out of cowardice or shyness, I choose diversion instead: 'It's funny, you know, Mum. I never used to read at all when I was a kid, did I? I had no interest in books or in reading whatsoever. That all came a lot later.'

'But you used to be good at art, and you were very interested in music too.'

I smile at her version of my version of my life.

'It's a fairly universal concept,' I state flatly, 'that, in any social group, there are always outcasts and misfits. As an example, in any school, in any class, there are always kids who are pushed to the margins: those who are maybe not good at sports, maybe less traditionally academic or just the spotty, ugly ones who can't get girlfriends. A strange awkward fate and circumstance bonds these misfits together. Together, they feel oddly empowered, often enough to form a band, for heaven's sake! But even in these cells of misfits, there are those who are pushed even further to the fringes. The ones who are not brainy enough to be the brains of the outfit, not mad enough to be the mad one or not corpulent enough to warrant the uninventive nickname. So that was me, basically – the misfit's misfit – solitarily lurking at the margins beyond the margins! But the truth is that you get a much better view of everything from out there. All the horror and the perversity and the vanity. It was probably around that time when I first thought about writing.'

'So, is it her?' she asks abruptly.

I pretend to not understand the question. 'Is what her?'

'Oh, come along, darling! Do you believe that Anne is your Platonic other – or your Aristotelian other, if you really insist?'

I pout in a manner that is possibly far more revealing than I might have intended, but I say nothing.

She continues, 'I mean, this would clearly be suggested by the overall narrative of your story so far. Do you think Anne is literally your *autre*, as you term it?'

I ponder for a moment before replying. 'I think,' I say cautiously, 'that if it is not her, then it will never be anybody else.'

She raises her eyes dramatically but catches herself before she vocalises her immediate response. 'But… I mean… In fairness, you have only known her for—'

'But it's like you said earlier, it all happens in an instant, and I know I felt something literally within minutes of meeting her – something ancient and antediluvian, and I felt I'd known her all my life. I knew everything about her, and she knew everything about me. We had no secrets and therefore no need to guard them. It just came over me like a sudden, blissful awareness – an utter certainty. Memory rather than anything as nebulous as an emotion. Instinct rather than experience. I ignored it and denied it, then desperately sought an alternative interpretation – desire, boredom, anything.'

My mother shifts in her chair slightly, but she says nothing.

'Or just that dreadful human urge to obscure the failure and the quiet despair that starts to engulf us after fifty. All those terrible orgies of need and the primitivism of our animal panic,' I conclude.

'Surely, there must always be some doubt?'

I shake my head slowly. 'She's only over there, and I miss the sense of her being proximate – I really do. I want to rush over and grab her hand. I miss the actual physical sense of her. When we sat down at this table just now, it felt strange to be seated opposite her. My every instinct was telling me I should be sitting alongside her; she should be next to me so our shoulders and perhaps even our knees might be in contact, and we would also be looking in the same direction and seeing the same things. Everything and anything that would suggest a greater sense of our unity. And by the way, it was Aristotle not Plato who defined love as a single soul occupying two bodies.'

The thing about talking to parents is that the urge to insert 'so there' into the conversation occasionally never entirely abandons you.

My mother makes a small noise and smiles again. 'Do you think she actually shares your... *ideas?*' She makes the word sound disreputable and perhaps even sordid.

'Sometimes, mainly by implication, but there does seem to be some awareness. She was the first one to notice how remarkably similar our hands are.'

'Oh, is that an official, recognisable signifier, then?'

There is a very thin path between sarcasm and mockery, which my mother has effortlessly navigated for as long as I can remember.

'I don't know. I just found it sort of interesting...' My voice trails off, and we lapse into a silence that is familiar rather than comfortable.

But then I am suddenly speaking again. 'Look, Mum,' I say in an animated, hurried manner, as though I am keen not to lose my train of thought or be interrupted again, 'I will never acquire enough material wealth so that I might be defined by my possessions or my acts of kindness. I will never do anything heroic or noteworthy or be great or significant or important in any way...'

She attempts to speak, but I silence her. 'No, Mum, hang on; hang on... just a moment. There will be no great achievements in my life to reflect upon as I lay dying, and no sense of satisfaction resulting from my fabulous, ancient triumphs and accomplishments. There will be nothing like that. But I promise you this, Mum: if I remember nothing else, I will so vividly recall

191

a feeling, and it is the unique, extraordinary one that will give my whole life clarity and meaning. Perhaps this is the means by which all lives should be judged: the recollection of its single greatest sensation. Because mine will be the feeling I have today, and I know it is one that will stay with me always. It's precisely that sense of *illumination* I experience whenever I think of Anne... or I see Anne... or...'

'Illumination? Well, maybe you should write—'

No, not now, I think.

'And the gratitude, Mum, that – regardless of what happens later today or tomorrow or indeed the rest of my life – I was once alive, truly alive, and I lived just long enough to feel this sense of wonder.

'This purpose to being.'

I feel a tear as I close my eyes, and I can see her face now.

When I open them again, my mother has gone and Anne is once again sitting opposite me.

And she is smiling at me.

I promise I never loved before you.
And if I ever did for a moment,
it was only that I loved an echo or a trace
of something which reminded me of you.

25. LOVE

So do we effectively have the slightest control over such things?

Does a man get to choose his obsessions?

Or is it more that his obsessions choose him?

I never seemed to make a conscious decision to fall under the spell of Rimbaud. Or to prostate myself at the feet of Robert Johnson. These things just sort of happened to me.

Maybe it's all in the timing.

Maybe our defining passions have a way of finding us when we most need them. They are a response, perhaps, to some psychological or emotional vacuum.

And now I can't help but think of Anne in the same way.

Is it possible that *love* is a response to a similar vacuum?

For a moment I lose myself in a sudden random thought, wondering if a *love vacuum* is A) a concept explored by Erich Fromm, B) a song by Buzzcocks or C) a product I'm recalling wrongly from a once glimpsed 1970's sex-aid catalogue.

'*On n'est pas sérieux, quand on a dix-sept ans...*'[42]

Or any combination of two digits, evidently.

---

42 No one is serious, when they are seventeen

But love is never frivolous.

So now I look at Anne, I study her face, and there are no theories or explanations for this.

Neither would I wish there to be.

Paradoxically, it is the very certainty of love that is its most terrifying aspect. The transfer of power to the object of your love, combined with the sure, certain knowledge that you will never love another. Or indeed have ever loved before. It is precisely the losing of this control that, ultimately, we both crave and fear. This is what we define as *'falling in love'* (the 'falling' implying the helplessness and absolute absence of will, device or agency), and at some point in the past twenty-four hours, I have fallen so hopelessly and desperately in love with Anne.

She is talking to me again now. I think I am listening, but I'm not sure. I am reasonably confident that I am hearing individual words and phrases, yet their meanings fluctuate and elude me, and I can only process the general mood – the overall sense of what she is saying. But it is the simplest and most basic form of interaction: she is smiling, and therefore I am happy.

If I find ever a god
Then I would only pray
For you and I to be the architects
Of all our numbered days.

Meanwhile, the raggedy teenager with the down-turned clay pipe approaches our table again. He sneers at me with his customary loathing, but this time he says nothing. I don't need his judgement or approval just now. He stands behind Anne's chair, resting a single hand on her shoulder. He fixes me with a stare, goading me to make my decision.

There are vague aspects to the scene that all but insist I recall those events of 21st July 1872.

The action that day took place in Brussels, where Verlaine's young wife and his mother attempted to stage what we would nowadays call an intervention. They had made the trip to Belgium, where Rimbaud and Verlaine had been staying, with the express purpose of wrestling their absent husband and son away from the literal and metaphorical clutches of the hooligan from Charleville. They met with Verlaine, and to their considerable credit, they managed to convince him of the error of his ways. He agreed to their demands and promised to abandon Rimbaud and travel back with them on the evening train to Paris.

Verlaine, unsurprisingly, spent the day becoming increasingly intoxicated, but he somehow managed to board the train at its scheduled departure time. The scene is all too easy to imagine. Verlaine was inebriated and rowdy, and when all the passengers disembarked at the border to pass through customs, he disappeared from the watchful gaze of his companions. When they returned to their seats on the train, they finally caught sight of him standing on the platform. 'I'm staying,' he shouted to them. Then they noticed that he was not alone – he had been joined by his disreputable friend once more. Rimbaud had jumped on the train in Brussels at the last moment and spent the past fifty miles hiding in the toilet.

This was Verlaine making his choice between what was constant and rational and the lure of *l'inconnu*. Maybe a great number of our life-defining decisions, perhaps all of them, have this precise dualistic conundrum at their core.

Anne now rises from her chair with a grace and quiet elegance she would rather I refrained from mentioning.

'Now,' she says, blandly.

I stand up quickly. 'Now?'

'Yes, come on, Marc. It is time.'

She walks briskly away from the table, glancing over her shoulder as she does so. I do not question her or ask anything of her any more; I simply follow her.

I genuinely feel I have no choice.

We walk hand in hand across La Place Ducale in the direction of the Rue du Petit-Bois; I look around me as though part of me can sense that I will wish to recall it one day.

There is a man who walks with a limp, but his beatific smile is genuine.

Outside the town, birds are now gathering at the entrance to a cave, they are silent, but their plumage is magnificent.

Three girls now hurry past me, and I smell the sweet summer odour of flowers on their skin.

There is an old man playing the same eight-note melody on a piano in a windowless attic room.

There is a girl somewhere on whose beautiful bare shoulders I once traced an infinity symbol with my forefinger.

There is a woman who has never known love, but she can write of a lover's caress in a way that would move any man to tears.

Beyond the far outskirts of the village, where the crops in the fields have failed for years and years, there are now angels grouped in small clusters around the neglected machinery and tractors.

There is a vast, dark abandoned house by a harbour where children play all day, but laughter is never heard.

A man called Johnson sings the blues, but the poetry is not in his words but in his life.

And then there is a wise and kind lady with her hair turning grey now, who took my hand when I had no need of her and then let it go when I did.

Everything else is just the fucking afternoon.

Anne and I walk a little further and then turn right into a quiet side road called Rue Pierre Gillet, which, to be perfectly honest, I have never noticed before.

Anne stops in front of a shuttered building and squeezes my hand tightly. 'We're here,' she says coyly, looking directly into my eyes and biting her bottom lip.

As though not wishing to disturb the unhurried tranquillity of the hour, she reaches slowly into her pocket for a key, takes it out and opens the door carefully. I follow her into an unlit hallway. I see dark wood, patterned wallpaper, a mirror, and umbrellas leaning against a chest of drawers.

I hear a dog in an upstairs room, and I can smell food and dust.

And ghosts.

Somewhere in the basement or in an adjacent room, I imagine there is a glass case with one or more stuffed animals – perhaps a snake and a mongoose – but of course, I have no way of knowing this.

Anne gestures with an upturned hand. 'You like? This is my friend's house. It is where I live at the moment.'

I smile and nod, but I can think of little to actually say. 'Oh right. It's very nice, isn't it? I mean it's got a lot of—'

Anne interrupts me and puts her finger to her lips. 'Shush… She is not back until later.' Her grin is knowing and conspiratorial. 'I have the house entirely to myself this afternoon.'

Then she takes both my hands in hers and pulls me towards her.

She kisses me.

Now I don't smell the ghosts any more.

I just smell the proximity of infinity.

26. Rapture

I follow Anne into the lounge. The shutters are closed, and I inhale sharply. But viewed internally, they take on a different aspect somehow, and I confess that I see them quite differently. Not as a barrier against light but as one against time – the hour of the day being of little or no consequence, given the merciless melancholy of the room.

Anne is arranging the pillows on the single guest bed that I presume to be hers as she talks to me. 'You see, Marc, the principle is so appealing and so romantic, but the numbers are wrong.'

'What numbers?'

She shakes the quilt. 'Well, if you imagine you have a single perfect *autre* and you are both descendants from the same ancient hermaphroditic source, then, over the centuries, those descendants would now number probably in the hundreds of thousands, surely?'

I frown, but the permanent twilight of the room means my grimace is unseen. 'I suppose so.'

'So surely that means if there are so many more possible

autres out there, then the odds of finding him or her decrease quite considerably. Would that not be true?'

'Of course.'

She smiles. 'So you see, technically, it's therefore far from impossible. Rather than finding a single person in the entire world, amongst the billion millions, it might be more like finding one in... yes, Charleville, maybe?'

Her logic is unequivocal, but I wonder how Yeats would respond to it. Then I steal a look at Anne as she pulls her T-shirt off over her head and I feel I know what he might have said:

Oh, let me die ignorant of your ways
And unknowing of your nature.
Let me die with this rapture intact...

'That is nice, Marc,' she says, her breasts now naked and exposed to me. Beyond beauty, which is clouded by subjective judgement and aesthetics, there is perfection, which is infinite and universal. Perhaps on account of some residual shyness on my part, I rest my gaze upon her eyes, in which I perceive not the slightest suggestion of provocation.

'I like that,' she confirms, 'I like the slightly jarring non-rhyme of "nature" and "rapture". It's actually reminiscent of Rimbaud.'

I notice that, with an almost maternal discretion, she now cups her right hand under her breast and then rubs her right nipple with her right thumb. The gesture seems more nervous in origin, self-conscious even, than deliberately seductive.

She smiles at me, as with urgency rather than ceremony, she removes her shorts and her underwear in quick succession. I feel the slight vibration in my lungs as I take a long, deep breath. The conceit of writers and the arrogance of poets, our vanities will always betray us. For in moments like this, we are rendered mute and useless. It is a true and clear reality, but it can never be accurately recalled.

This exists, but it never existed.

I keep my eyes on her face, but I find myself mapping the outline of her shoulders, the line of her breasts, her tummy and the shadow between her legs.

And the shadow between her legs...

She takes a step towards me and kisses me. I taste her and I love her and I need her and I feel off-balance and nervous. A sensation that I might have once interpreted as fear or apprehension grips me, and I recognise that kissing her in Parc Pierquin was not a star but simply the arc that preceded it. That preceded this. I have a sudden moment of clarity, and I understand that, in a shuttered room, it is not the darkness; it is the person with whom you share the darkness.

I feel her tongue pushing into my mouth as I sense her hand on mine. She pulls it towards her and places it over her crotch, and I feel the warmth and the stubble and the dampness. It is generally recognised, I think, that 'seductress' is possibly the most beautiful word in the English language, and the only reason it features so infrequently in the poetry of this or any other age is because nothing actually rhymes with it...

'Marc?'

'Yes...'

'Not now...'

She pushes her hand into my trousers, and I feel it now tightening its grip on my cock as it grows heavy and hard. I have not felt aroused like this in ages, perhaps ever. She pulls me towards her; grabbing its tip and brushing my hand aside, she slips it between her legs. She exhales in a sudden short burst, and I feel her breath on my cheek. Next, I feel the glow of her skin, her heat. I taste her mouth and the sweat on her neck. I feel my cock pushing against her; my eyes close, yet I can still see her.

I feel her nakedness on mine. There are shadows now, shapes, angles; there are clothes on the floor – my clothes, discarded, irrelevant, historic. I feel the hardness of her nipples as they press against mine, lining up so perfectly, and I feel a pulse. Then I feel a second alongside it, and like a child who cannot differentiate between fear and excitement, I find that I have no real need or wish to do so. I feel her rhythms now, so strongly: it is in the way she walks, the manner in which she speaks, the tilt of her head, the angle of her lip when she smiles, and the way she girlishly kicks her heels as she leads me towards the bed.

And there she is now.

And next the ceremony.

The ritual.

The confession.

If the hand that had pulled the trigger was yours,
Then dying, I would still crawl across the floor to kiss it.

'Then kiss me, Marc!'

She lies on the bed and opens her legs, giving me an unobstructed view. Once again I find I am totally unprepared for my own response. It is not this, for this I know, but it is the scale of this. I feel that same pulsing in my chest once more and then that second echo again, fractionally behind it. Gradually, they merge into a single steady beat as I throw myself on top of Anne.

I am aware I should reflect upon restraint at this point, timing and technique and all those things that might translate into consideration or sensitivity in the mind of a new partner. But I feel now that I am being driven by some ancient instinct I can barely understand or even comprehend. Something so biologically pure and raw that all cognitive processes are rendered obsolete and redundant.

I see her eyes widen, and I feel her body tensing as I push myself into her. For a fleeting moment, I think that I can see us almost as a geometrical cross-section; as two perfectly matched curves – two arcs, echoing with faultless accuracy those in the skies above us, the golden chains that link us together for all time.

I push her knees back a little, and my cock slips in even deeper. I inhale sharply and shudder at precisely the same moment she does.

She sinks her teeth into my shoulder.

'Marc,' she whispers my name as I silently mouth hers.

I have a sudden wave of awareness, a consciousness of all things; I am thrown onto a timeline that stretches back to the very moment of my own conception, and I feel I might die at any moment. Yet if this is to be the manner of my death, then it is the one I would have chosen. I feel her muscles contract as she grips me tighter, and then I lose myself. What I lose specifically is the awareness of what is her and what is me; where I end and she begins. My very existence seems questionable, optional, variable. I can still feel my cock, but somehow, I know I can also feel it inside me, pushing into me.

'Marc, what is happening?'

I hear the question, but I swear I could also feel the words forming in my mouth as I uttered them. I glance to my right, and he is there in the shadows; I scan his face for an expression of sympathy, but all I see is revulsion. I wait in vain for his words, but I doubt I would hear them any more.

It is too late now.

No mother now, no sense of family, heritage or tradition; no sense of country or culture; and very little awareness of who I actually am.

As I feel her warmth closing around me, at the very epicentre of us, I realise that this is the only place I will ever call...

'Home.'

The voice is still mine, but it is not wholly mine now. Pitched fractionally higher than before, it now defines and is synonymous with the first word it uttered and quickly repeats.

'Home.'

Harmony is that pleasing difference between notes heard simultaneously. But to shift a star upon its axis, one requires the precision of two identical tones overlaid upon each other, neither one being dominant or secondary, and the creation of the single perfect unique vibration. The purity and the glory remain for all time in that most simple of qualities.

I close my eyes and I open them. I see his face and then I see her face, then his, then hers, and then, suddenly, I see neither and I realise that I am both. I understand now what separation truly means. To completely grasp the concept you must first experience its diametric opposite. Aristotle understood this, but we chose to ignore him for too long.

But now...

It is not accurate to say that I am no longer female, for a part of me will always be female. It is simply that from this moment onwards I am also male.

'Home.'

Not a linear process or a single sudden moment, but rather a sequence of fragmented, disjointed events heralding a shift in all realities and all definitions. I, she, he, we – these are hasty, superficial terms of convenience, outdated now and of little relevance. All the words in the world are cold, restrictive and mechanical except...

'Je est un autre.'

No, Rimbaud! You are a seer, but you are young too.

And foolish!

And wrong! You see, there are not 'all kinds of madness'!

There never was!

There is just one.

And it is this one!

No, no, no. You were not too young! You just didn't live long enough! You talk of love, of suffering, of madness – d'amour, de souffrance, de folie – but I know for a fact there is no tangible distinction between them. Not here! Not now! Not any more! The greatest star of all is the point at which those three golden chains intersect. You see, I am nothing now except my understanding of this, the true and real sense of this!

'*Je est un autre.*'

'*Je est* Anne Autry.'

For who, if not Rimbaud, would write verses and daub slogans to welcome these new gods?

I reach out for a hand as I approach orgasm, but there is no other hand there now – just the one.

I lean forwards to make contact with that beautiful mouth, but it is also absent. Yet so clearly present.

I see our chest, our two nipples, and glance down towards our now dormant sex organ, but I see just the one bright, shining star.

In its light, I see the single shadow we cast upon the wall.

All is silent aside from our racing heartbeat.

One… *two.*

One… *two…*

'Home.'

Everything else is just dust.

Hôtel Couleurs Sud, Charleville-Mézières. 7th June 2022. P.L.P.